Maths Call

Developing children's listening skills in the Daily Maths Lesson

YEAR
5

Peter Clarke

Published by Collins Educational

An imprint of HarperCollins*Publishers* Ltd

77-85 Fulham Palace Road

Hammersmith

London

W6 8JB

www.**Collins**Education.com
On-line Support for Schools and Colleges

First published 2002

ISBN 0 00 713355 3

Cover design by Caroline Grimshaw
Cover illustration by Andrew Hamilton
Series design by Neil Adams
Illustrations by Bethan Matthews, Jeffrey Reid, Rhiannon Powell, Tim Archbold.

Printed by Martins the Printers, Berwick on Tweed

Contents

Introduction

Maths Call is a series of seven books from Reception to Year 6 which is designed to assist children to practise and consolidate objectives from the National Numeracy Strategy (NNS) *Framework for Teaching Mathematics* at the same time as developing their listening skills.

Listening and following instructions are two key skills that are crucial to the success of every child and every adult. How many times have children had to redo work because they have not listened to your directions? How many times do you have to repeat yourself? How often have you wished you could take time out from the overburdened curriculum to help children develop their listening skills? This series will help you solve these problems. You will not have to take time away from other curriculum areas to do this since *Maths Call* helps to develop children's listening skills and ability to follow oral directions while they practise valuable mathematical skills.

Listening and communicating

The purpose of this book is the development of children's listening skills through the mathematics curriculum, but this skill is not seen in isolation. Many of the activities outlined include reading, speaking and writing. Listening is an integral part of communication which deals with the process of giving and receiving information. The four different aspects of the communication process outlined below rely upon each other for effective communication at the same time as actively supporting and enriching one another.

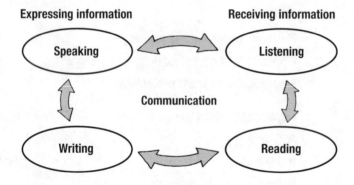

Communication and mental imagery

All children, whatever their age and ability, have their own mental images, developed from previous knowledge and experiences. Aural stimulus enables children to manipulate the mental images they have of numbers, shapes and measures. Instant recall of number facts such as the multiplication tables and the addition and subtraction number facts often depends on an aural input. Children have to hear the sounds in order to give an automatic response.

The difficult part for the teacher is to discover what is going on inside children's heads. This is where discussion as an accompaniment to mental work is so important. It is only through discussion that the teacher can begin to develop an insight into children's mental processes. Discussions also enable children to develop their own insights into their mental imagery and provide the opportunity for them to share their ideas and methods. They can form judgements about the alternatives, decide which methods are the most efficient and effective for them, and further develop flexibility and familiarity with the different mathematical topics.

The skills of listening

Listening skills can be improved through training and practice. When direct attention is paid to listening for specific purposes, and these skills are practised and consolidated, improvement in ability follows. In general children tend to learn and remember more through listening than in almost any other way. A high percentage of all the information children receive comes through their ears. Thus direct training in the skills of listening can be hugely beneficial to all learning.

Effective listening involves:
- hearing
- concentrating
- a knowledge of language
- a knowledge of the structure of language
- recognising cues
- being able to contextualise
- inferring
- thinking
- processing
- summarising
- selecting
- organising
- drawing upon previous knowledge and experience
- comprehending/understanding the main idea.

Becoming a good listener

Display the poster on page 6 to remind children of how to become a good listener. When concentrating on developing children's listening skills draw attention to the poster.

Characteristics of a good listener

A good listener is one who:
- knows how to listen
- is able to concentrate on listening
- looks at the speaker
- is courteous to the speaker
- does not interrupt the speaker
- is able to zero in on the speaker and eliminate extraneous noises and interruptions
- can comprehend
- is selective
- asks him/herself questions while listening
- draws upon their previous knowledge and experiences
- evaluates while listening
- remembers what is said
- anticipates what is coming next.

Good listening

Sit still

Think about the words

Look at the speaker

Maths Call and the teaching–learning cycle

Assessment
- Each activity can be used to assess a specific objective from the NNS *Framework*.
- Guidance given on how to record pupil performance.

Planning
- Each activity linked to an objective in the NNS *Framework*.
- Guidance given for planning a programme of work.

Teaching
- Clear and complete instructions given for each activity.
- Ideally suited to the daily mathematics lesson.

Curriculum information

Each of the 30 activities is organised under specific objectives as identified in the NNS *Framework*. The *Maths Call* objectives coverage chart on pages 8 and 9 shows which activity is matched to which objective(s).

Planning a programme of work for *Maths Call*

The *Maths Call* programme chart on page 10 may be used in conjunction with your long- and medium-term plans to develop a *Maths Call* programme of work throughout the year. By following the topics allocated using the NNS *Framework* or a similar scheme of work you will ensure that the children have the opportunity to practise and consolidate the topic, and specific objectives for a particular week, at the same time as developing their listening skills.

Maths Call and the daily mathematics lesson

The activities contained in *Maths Call* are ideally suited to the daily mathematics lesson. Each activity is designed to be presented to the whole class. The activities are extremely flexible and can be used in a variety of ways. For example, activities can be used during the:
- oral work and mental calculation session to practise and consolidate previously taught concepts;
- main teaching part of the lesson to focus on particular skills and concepts;
- plenary session to consolidate the concept(s) taught during the main part of the lesson and to conclude the lesson in an enjoyable way.

Maths Call objectives coverage

STRAND	TOPIC	OBJECTIVES	ACTIVITY	PAGE
Numbers and the number system	Place value, ordering and rounding	Multiply and divide any positive integer up to 10 000 by 10 or 100 and understand the effect (e.g. $9900 \div 10$, $737 \div 10$, $2060 \div 100$).	1	12
		Use the vocabulary of comparing and ordering numbers, including symbols such as $<$, $>$, $\leq$, $\geq$, $=$. Give one or more numbers lying between two given numbers. Order a set of integers less than 1 million. Order a given set of positive and negative integers (e.g. on a number line, on a temperature scale).	2	14
		Round any integer up to 10 000 to the nearest 10, 100 or 1000.	3	16
	Properties of numbers and number sequences	Recognise and extend number sequences formed by counting from any number in steps of constant size, extending beyond zero when counting back. For example: – count on in steps of 25 to 1000, and then back; – count on or back in steps of 0.1, 0.2, 0.3…	4	18
		Recognise multiples of 6, 7, 8, 9, up to the 10th multiple. Know squares of numbers to at least 10×10. Find all the pairs of factors of any number up to 100.	5	20
	Fractions, decimals and percentages	Change an improper fraction to a mixed number (e.g. change $\frac{13}{10}$ to $1\frac{3}{10}$). Recognise when two simple fractions are equivalent, including relating hundredths to tenths (e.g. $\frac{70}{100} = \frac{7}{10}$). Order a set of fractions such as 2, $2\frac{3}{4}$, $1\frac{3}{4}$, $2\frac{1}{2}$, $1\frac{1}{2}$, and position them on a number line.	6	22
		Relate fractions to division, and use division to find simple fractions, including tenths and hundredths, of numbers and quantities (e.g. $\frac{3}{4}$ of 12, $\frac{1}{10}$ of 50, $\frac{1}{100}$ of £3).	7	24
		Know what each digit represents in a number with up to two decimal places. Order a set of numbers or measurements with the same number of decimal places. Round a number with one or two decimal places to the nearest integer.	8	26
		Relate fractions to their decimal representations: that is, recognise the equivalence between the decimal and fraction forms of one half, one quarter, three quarters… and tenths and hundredths (e.g. $\frac{7}{10} = 0.7$, $\frac{27}{100} = 0.27$).	9	28
		Begin to understand percentage as the number of parts in every 100, and find simple percentages of small whole-number quantities (e.g. 25% of 8).	10	30
Calculations	Addition and subtraction	Derive quickly or continue to derive quickly: – decimals that total 1 (e.g. $0.2 + 0.8$) or 10 (e.g. $6.2 + 3.8$); – all two-digit pairs that total 100 (e.g. $43 + 57$); – all pairs of multiples of 50 with a total of 1000 (e.g. $350 + 650$).	11	32
		Use known number facts and place value for mental addition and subtraction (e.g. $470 + 380$, $810 - 380$, $7.4 + 9.8$, $9.2 - 8.6$).	12	34
		Use informal pencil and paper methods to support, record or explain additions and subtractions. Extend written methods to column addition/subtraction of two integers less than 10 000.	13	36
		Use informal pencil and paper methods to support, record or explain additions and subtractions. Extend written methods to addition or subtraction of a pair of decimal fractions, both with one or both with two decimal places (e.g. £29.78 + £53.34).	14	38

STRAND	TOPIC	OBJECTIVES	ACTIVITY	PAGE
Calculations *continued*	Addition	Use informal pencil and paper methods to support, record or explain additions. Extend written methods to addition of more than two integers less than 10 000.	15	40
	Multiplication	Know by heart all multiplication facts up to 10 × 10.	16	42
		Use informal pencil and paper methods to support, record or explain multiplications. Extend written methods to short multiplication of HTU or U.t by U.	17	44
		Use informal pencil and paper methods to support, record or explain multiplications. Extend written methods to long multiplication of TU by TU.	18	46
	Division	Derive quickly or continue to derive quickly division facts corresponding to tables up to 10 × 10.	19	48
		Use informal pencil and paper methods to support, record or explain divisions. Extend written methods to short division of HTU by U (with integer remainder).	20	50
	Multiplication and division	Derive quickly or continue to derive quickly: – doubles of all whole numbers 1 to 100 (e.g. 78 × 2); – doubles of multiples of 10 to 1000 (e.g. 670 × 2); – doubles of multiples of 100 to 10 000 (e.g. 6500 × 2); – and the corresponding halves.	21	52
		Use known facts and place value to multiply and divide mentally.	22	54
Solving problems	Problems involving 'real life' and measures	Use all four operations to solve simple word problems involving numbers and quantities based on 'real life' and measures, using one or more steps.	23	56
	Problems involving money	Use all four operations to solve simple word problems involving numbers and quantities based on money, using one or more steps, including making simple conversions of pounds to foreign currency and finding simple percentages.	24	58
Measures	Length, mass and capacity	Use, read and write standard metric units (km, m, cm, mm, kg, g, l, ml), including their abbreviations, and relationships between them. Convert larger to smaller units (e.g. km to m, m to cm or mm, kg to g, l to ml). Know imperial units (mile, pint, gallon).	25	60
	Area and perimeter	Understand area measured in square centimetres (cm^2). Understand and use the formula in words 'length × breadth' for the area of a rectangle. Understand, measure and calculate perimeters of rectangles and regular polygons.	26	62
	Time	Read the time on a 24-hour digital clock and use 24-hour clock notation, such as 19:53.	27	64
		Use timetables.	28	66
Shape and space	Reflective symmetry	Complete symmetrical patterns with two lines of symmetry at right angles (using squared paper or pegboard).	29	68
	Position and direction	Read and plot co-ordinates in the first quadrant.	30	70

Maths Call programme

YEAR
CLASS
TEACHER

	WEEK	TOPIC	*MATHS CALL* ACTIVITY
AUTUMN	1		
	2		
	3		
	4		
	5		
	6		
	7		
	8		
	9		
	10		
	11		
	12		
SPRING	1		
	2		
	3		
	4		
	5		
	6		
	7		
	8		
	9		
	10		
	11		
	12		
SUMMER	1		
	2		
	3		
	4		
	5		
	6		
	7		
	8		
	9		
	10		
	11		
	12		

How to use *Maths Call*

Preparation

- Provide each child with the necessary resources. These can be found at the beginning of each activity's teacher's page.

Instructions

Explain the following to the children:

- They need to listen carefully.
- They will be given some oral instructions to follow.
- The instructions will only be given once.
- They must only do what they are told to do, nothing more.
- They may not use an eraser.
- How many instructions there are for the particular activity.
- That they are to do each task immediately after the instructions for that part have been given.

The activity

- If necessary, briefly discuss the pupil sheet with the children. Ensure that the children are familiar with the pictures and/or the text on the sheet.
- Ensure that the children are also familiar with any of the terms used in the oral instructions. Refer to the *Key words* for a list of the relevant vocabulary.
- Ask the children to write the date on the sheet in the space provided.
- Do not ask the children to write their name. This will occur during the activity.
- Slowly read the instructions to the children.

Discussion

- After the children have completed the sheet, discuss the activity with the class. You may decide to do this either before or after marking the activity. Use the *Discussion questions* as a springboard. For each activity there are questions that have been designed to cater for higher attaining (↑) and lower attaining (↓) pupils.

Marking

- Mark the sheet with the whole class, either before or after the discussion. You may wish the children to mark their own sheet or to swap with someone next to them. However, if you are using the activity as an assessment tool then you may decide to mark the sheets yourself at a later stage.

Revisiting an activity

- Repeat an activity with the class at a later stage in the year. Children can compare how they performed on the task the second time round.
- You may like to alter the activity slightly by changing one or two of the instructions.

Maths Call and assessment

Maths Call activities may be used with the whole class or with groups of children as an assessment activity. Linked to the topic that is being studied at present, *Maths Call* will provide you with an indication of how well the children have understood the objectives being covered as well as how their listening skills are developing. The *Maths Call* assessment sheet on page 72 may be used to record how well the children have understood the objectives covered in the activity.

Place value, ordering and rounding

- Multiply and divide any positive integer up to 10 000 by 10 or 100 and understand the effect (e.g. 9900 ÷ 10, 737 ÷ 10, 2060 ÷ 100).

Resources

Provide each child with the following:
- a copy of Activity 1 pupil sheet
- a red, blue, green and yellow coloured pencil

Key words

zero, one, two… ten thousand   multiplied by   times   product
divided by   one tenth   one hundredth

Say to the children:

Listen carefully.

I am going to tell you some things to do.

I will say them only once, so listen very carefully.

Do only the things you are told to do and nothing else.

If you make a mistake, cross it out. Do not use an eraser.

There are 13 parts to this activity.

The activity

1. What is 634 multiplied by 10? Find that number and colour it red.

2. What is 73 times one hundred? Find that number and colour it red.

3. What is 121 times 10? Find that number and colour it blue.

4. What is the product of 95 and 100? Find that number and colour it blue.

5. What is 4800 divided by 10? Find that number and colour it green.

6. What is 730 divided by 10? Find that number and colour it green.

7. What is one hundredth of 730? Find that number and colour it yellow.

8. What is 1210 divided by 100? Find that number and colour it yellow.

9. What is one tenth of 1210? Find that number and colour it red.

10. What is 48 divided by 100? Find that number and colour it blue.

11. What is 52 times 10? Find that number and colour it green.

12. What is the product of 100 and 5200? Find that number and colour it yellow.

13. What is one tenth of 950? Find that number and write your name under that number.

Answers

Discussion questions

↓ What colour is the number 480? (green)

↓ Tell me a number you did not colour? (0.52, 4.8, 9.5, 634, 730, 950, 4800, 12 100, 52 000, 63 400, 480 000)

■ Choose a number on the sheet and multiply it/divide it by 10/100.

■ Which numbers did you colour red? (121, 6340, 7300)

↑ Look at the number 52 000. What is 52 000 divided by 10/100/1000? (5200/520/52)

↑ Look at the number 0.52. What is 0.52 multiplied by 10/100/1000? (5.2/52/520)

Place value, ordering and rounding

■ Multiply and divide any positive integer up to 10 000 by 10 or 100 and understand the effect (e.g. 9900 ÷ 10, 737 ÷ 10, 2060 ÷ 100).

Date _____

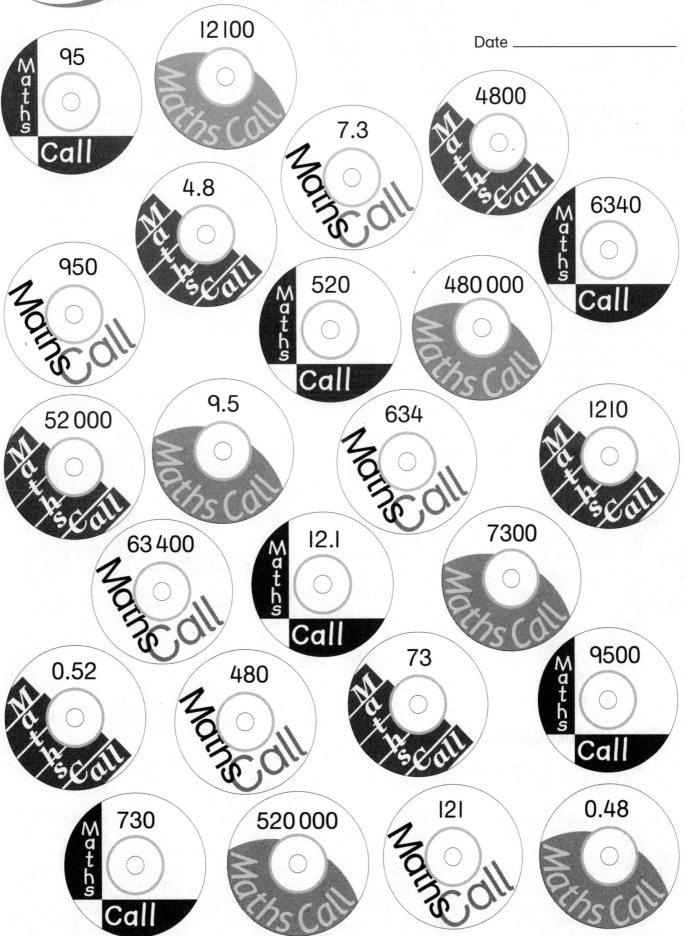

Year 5 Numbers and the number system

Place value, ordering and rounding

- Use the vocabulary of comparing and ordering numbers, including symbols such as $<, >, \leq, \geq, =$.
- Give one or more numbers lying between two given numbers.
- Order a set of integers less than 1 million.
- Order a given set of positive and negative integers (e.g. on a number line, on a temperature scale).

Resources

Provide each child with the following:
- a copy of Activity 2 pupil sheet
- a pencil

Key words

zero, one, two…one million   smallest   largest   less than   fewer than   more than   greater than   equal to   statement   true   first   second

Say to the children:

Listen carefully.

I am going to tell you some things to do.

I will say them only once, so listen very carefully.

Do only the things you are told to do and nothing else.

If you make a mistake, cross it out. Do not use an eraser.

There are 11 parts to this activity.

The activity

1. Look at question one. Write the number 93 in the box. Now write any number in the circle to make the statement true.
2. Look at question two. Write the number 796 in the box. Now write any number in the circle to make the statement true.
3. Look at question three. Write the number 4203 in the box. Now write any number in the circle to make the statement true.
4. Look at question four. Write the number 56 104 in the box. Now write any number in the circle to make the statement true.
5. Look at question five. Write the number 14 209 in the box and the number 14 165 in the triangle. Now write any number in the circle to make the statement true.
6. Look at the set of numbers above the first number line. Write these numbers in order smallest to largest in the boxes below the number line.
7. Look at the set of numbers above the second number line. Write these numbers in order smallest to largest in the boxes below the number line.
8. Look at the first set of number cards. Write a number on each blank card so that the four numbers are in order.
9. Look at the second set of number cards. Write a number on each blank card so that the five numbers are in order.
10. Look at the numbers in the rings. Write these numbers in order smallest to largest in the rings at the bottom of the sheet.
11. Write your name above the date.

Answers

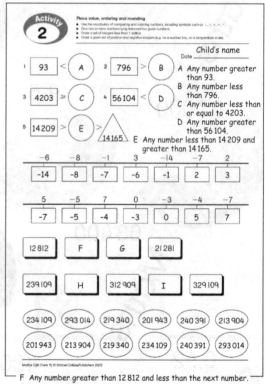

F Any number greater than 12 812 and less than the next number.
G Any number greater than the previous number and less than 21 281.
H Any number greater than 239 109 and less than 312 909.
I Any number greater than 312 909 and less than 329 109.

Discussion questions

↓ Look at the first question. What number did you write in the box/circle? (93/any number greater than 93) Read me the statement.

↓ Look at the first number line. Tell me the numbers in order largest to smallest? (3, 2, −1, −6, −7, −8, −14)

■ Look at question five. What number did you write in the circle? (any number less than 14 209 and greater than 14 165) Read me the statement.

■ Look at the numbers in the rings. Tell me these numbers in order smallest to largest. (201 943, 213 904, 219 340, 234 109, 240 391, 293 014)

↑ Write on the board a statement similar to question five. (e.g. 12 837 > 12 387 > 12 127; 347 912 < 437 829 < 473 829)

↑ Look at the first set of number cards. What numbers did you write on the blank number cards? (1st card – any number greater than 12 812 and less than the next number; 2nd card – any number greater than the previous number and less than 21 281.) What are some other numbers you could have written? (Answer same as above.)

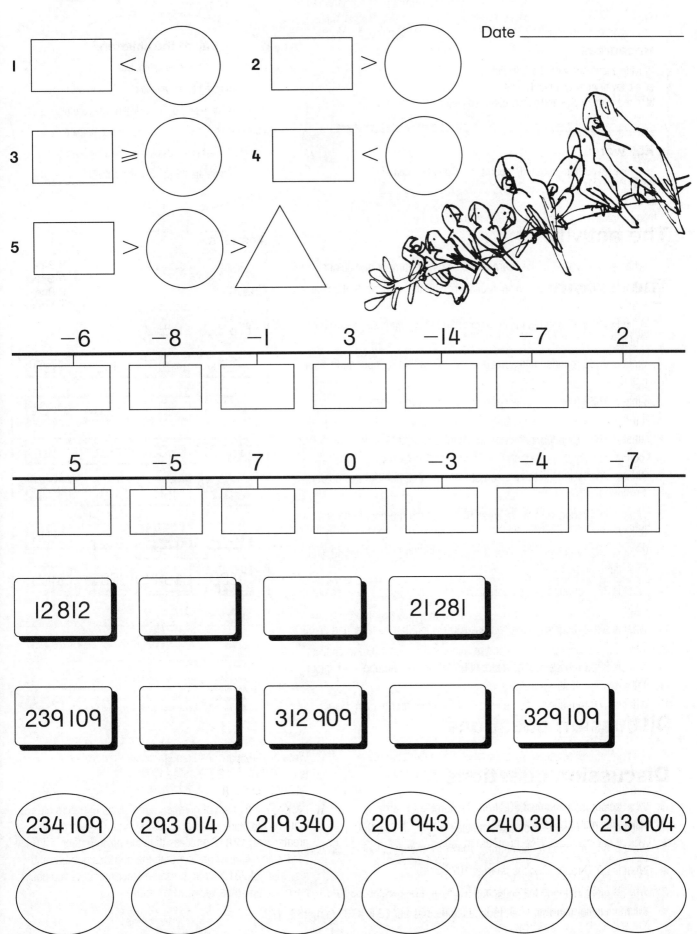

Activity 2

Place value, ordering and rounding

- Use the vocabulary of comparing and ordering numbers, including symbols such as <, >, ≤, ≥, =.
- Give one or more numbers lying between two given numbers.
- Order a set of integers less than 1 million.
- Order a given set of positive and negative integers (e.g. on a number line, on a temperature scale).

Date _____

1 ☐ < ◯

2 ☐ > ◯

3 ☐ ≥ ◯

4 ☐ < ◯

5 ☐ > ◯ > △

| −6 | −8 | −1 | 3 | −14 | −7 | 2 |

| 5 | −5 | 7 | 0 | −3 | −4 | −7 |

12 812   ☐   ☐   21 281

239 109   ☐   312 909   ☐   329 109

234 109   293 014   219 340   201 943   240 391   213 904

Activity 3

Place value, ordering and rounding
■ Round any integer up to 10 000 to the nearest 10, 100 or 1000.

Resources
Provide each child with the following:
■ a copy of Activity 3 pupil sheet
■ a red, blue, green and yellow coloured pencil

Key words
zero, one, two…ten thousand   round   rounded to   nearest

Say to the children:
Listen carefully.
I am going to tell you some things to do.
I will say them only once, so listen very carefully.
Do only the things you are told to do and nothing else.
If you make a mistake, cross it out. Do not use an eraser.
There are 13 parts to this activity.

The activity

1. What is 26 rounded to the nearest 10? Find that number and colour it red.
2. What is 346 rounded to the nearest 100? Find that number and colour it red.
3. What is 7804 rounded to the nearest 1000? Find that number and colour it blue.
4. What is 4033 rounded to the nearest 100? Find that number and colour it blue.
5. What is 1632 rounded to the nearest 10? Find that number and colour it green.
6. What is 1631 rounded to the nearest 1000? Find that number and colour it green.
7. What is 2015 rounded to the nearest 10? Find that number and colour it yellow.
8. What is 784 rounded to the nearest 100? Find that number and colour it yellow.
9. What is 5426 rounded to the nearest 1000? Find that number and write your name under it.
10. What is 351 rounded to the nearest 100? Find that number and colour it red.
11. What is 9292 rounded to the nearest 1000? Find that number and colour it blue.
12. What is 8263 rounded to the nearest 100? Find that number and colour it green.
13. What is 478 rounded to the nearest 10? Find that number and colour it yellow.

Answers

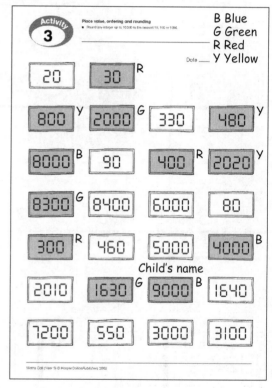

Discussion questions

↓ What colour is the number 30? (red)
↓ Tell me all the numbers you coloured blue? (4000, 8000, 9000)
■ What is 346 rounded to the nearest 100? (300) What colour is 300? (red)
■ What is 2015 rounded to the nearest 10? (2020)
↑ What is 8263 rounded to the nearest 10/100/1000? (8260/8300/8000)
↑ Tell me any number that when rounded to the nearest 10 is 470? (e.g. 466, 473)

Place value, ordering and rounding

■ Round any integer up to 10 000 to the nearest 10, 100 or 1000.

Date _____

20	30

800	2000	330	480
8000	90	400	2020
8300	8400	6000	80
300	460	5000	4000
2010	1630	9000	1640
7200	550	3000	3100

Year 5 Numbers and the number system

Properties of numbers and number sequences

■ Recognise and extend number sequences formed by counting from any number in steps of constant size, extending beyond zero when counting back. For example:
 – count on in steps of 25 to 1000, and then back;
 – count on or back in steps of 0.1, 0.2, 0.3…

Resources

Provide each child with the following:
■ a copy of Activity 4 pupil sheet
■ a red, blue and green coloured pencil
■ a ruler

Key words

zero, one, two…ten thousand   next   decimal   decimal point
sequence   steps   constant

Say to the children:

Listen carefully.

I am going to tell you some things to do.

I will say them only once, so listen very carefully.

Do only the things you are told to do and nothing else.

If you make a mistake, cross it out. Do not use an eraser.

There are 13 parts to this activity.

The activity

1. Put your red pencil on the letter B. Listen carefully as I count: 2500, 2600, 2700, 2800, 2900. What number comes next? Find that number and rule a red line from B to that number.

2. Put your green pencil on the letter C. 73, 69, 65, 61, 57. What number comes next? Find that number and rule a green line from C to that number.

3. Put your red pencil on the letter D. 25, 50, 75, 100, 125. What number comes next? Find that number and rule a red line from D to that number.

4. Put your blue pencil on the letter D. 18, 24, 30, 36, 42. What number comes next? Find that number and rule a blue line from D to that number.

5. Put your green pencil on the letter A. 4.6, 4.4, 4.2, 4, 3.8. What number comes next? Find that number and rule a green line from A to that number.

6. Put your green pencil on the letter B. 300, 275, 250, 225, 200. What number comes next? Find that number and rule a green line from B to that number.

7. Put your red pencil on the letter A. 7453, 7443, 7433, 7423, 7413. What number comes next? Find that number and rule a red line from A to that number.

8. Put your red pencil on the letter C. 4.3, 4.2, 4.1, 4, 3.9. What number comes next? Find that number and rule a red line from C to that number.

9. Put your green pencil on the letter D. 650, 675, 700, 725, 750. What number comes next? Find that number and rule a green line from D to that number.

10. Put your blue pencil on the letter C. 0.3, 0.5, 0.7, 0.9, 1.1. What number comes next? Find that number and rule a blue line from C to that number.

11. Put your blue pencil on the letter B. 100, 91, 82, 73, 64. What number comes next? Find that number and rule a blue line from B to that number.

12. Put your blue pencil on the letter A. 2640, 3640, 4640, 5640, 6640. What number comes next? Find that number and rule a blue line from A to that number.

13. Write your name in the centre of the pattern.

Answers

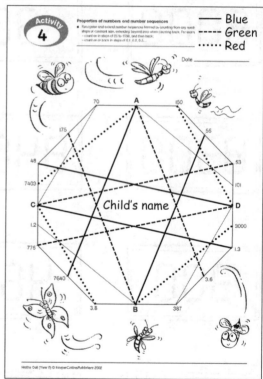

Discussion questions

↓ Which numbers have a green line going to them? (3.6, 53, 175, 775)

↓ Look at the number 55. What colour line have you drawn to that number? (blue)

■ Give me a number sequence. What is the next number? What is the rule?

■ Start at 3.4 and count on in twos. (3.4, 5.4, 7.4, 9.4.) What do you notice? (The tenths remain the same and the units increase by 2.)

↑ Give me a number sequence involving decimals. What is the next number? What is the rule?

↑ Look at the numbers around the octagon. Choose one of these and put it into a number sequence. What is the next number? What is the rule?

Properties of numbers and number sequences

■ Recognise and extend number sequences formed by counting from any number in steps of constant size, extending beyond zero when counting back. For example:
– count on in steps of 25 to 1000, and then back;
– count on or back in steps of 0.1, 0.2, 0.3…

Date _____

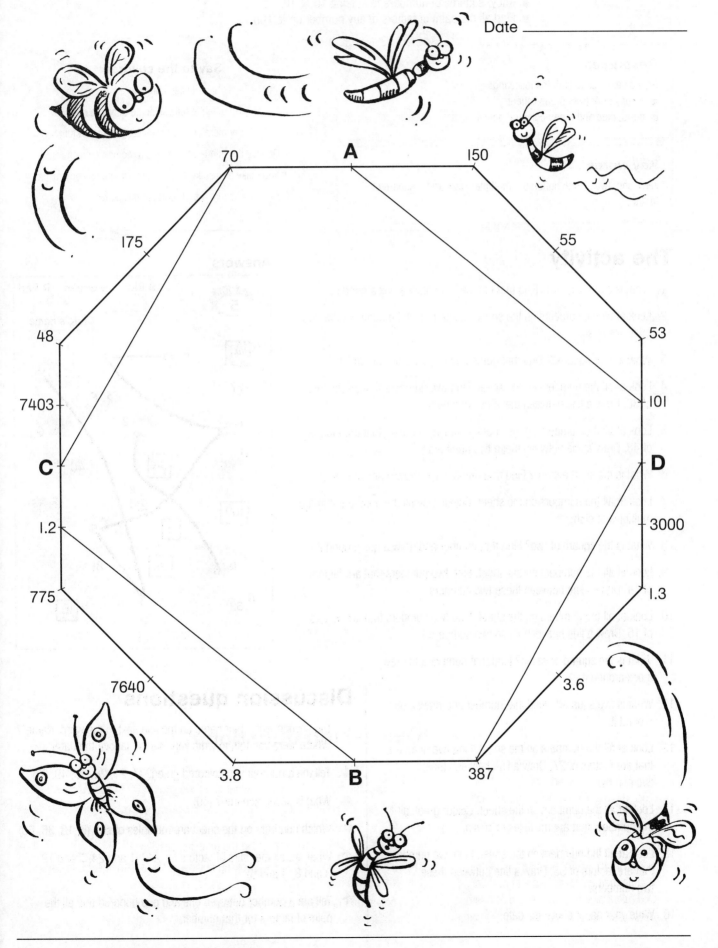

Properties of numbers and number sequences

- Recognise multiples of 6, 7, 8, 9, up to the 10th multiple.
- Know squares of numbers to at least 10 × 10.
- Find all the pairs of factors of any number up to 100.

Resources

Provide each child with the following:
- a copy of Activity 5 pupil sheet
- a red, blue and green coloured pencil

Key words

zero, one, two… one hundred   multiple   squared   square of
factor

Say to the children:

Listen carefully.

I am going to tell you some things to do.

I will say them only once, so listen very carefully.

Do only the things you are told to do and nothing else.

If you make a mistake, cross it out. Do not use an eraser.

There are 16 parts to this activity.

The activity

1. What is eight squared? Find that number and draw a box around it.

2. Look at all the numbers on the sheet. Colour red all the numbers that are multiples of six.

3. What is four squared? Find that number and draw a box around it.

4. Look at all the numbers on the sheet. Find two numbers that are factors of 36. Draw a line between these two numbers.

5. Look at all the numbers on the sheet. Find two numbers that are factors of 48. Draw a line between these two numbers.

6. What is the square of 10? Find that number and draw a box around it.

7. Look at all the numbers on the sheet. Colour blue all the numbers that are multiples of eight.

8. What is the square of two? Find that number and draw a box around it.

9. Look at all the numbers on the sheet. Find two numbers that are factors of 14. Draw a line between these two numbers.

10. Look at all the numbers on the sheet. Find two numbers that are factors of 15. Draw a line between these two numbers.

11. What is the square of seven? Find that number and draw a box around it.

12. What is five squared? Find that number and draw a box around it.

13. Look at all the numbers on the sheet. Find two numbers that are factors of 27. Draw a line between these two numbers.

14. Look at all the numbers on the sheet. Colour green all the numbers that are multiples of seven.

15. Look at all the numbers on the sheet. Find two numbers that are factors of 35. Draw a line between these two numbers.

16. Write your name above the date.

Answers

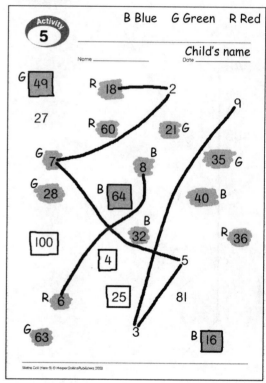

Discussion questions

↓ Did anyone write their name on the line next to the word 'Name'? Where were you told to write your name? (above the date)

↓ Tell me a number you coloured green? (7, 21, 28, 35, 49, 63)

■ What is seven squared? (49)

■ Which numbers on the sheet are multiples of six? (6, 18, 36, 60)

↑ What are all the pairs of factors for 24? (1 and 24, 2 and 12, 3 and 8, 4 and 6)

↑ Tell me a number between one and one hundred and all the pairs of factors for that number.

Activity
5

Properties of numbers and number sequences

- Recognise multiples of 6, 7, 8, 9, up to the 10th multiple.
- Know squares of numbers to at least 10 × 10.
- Find all the pairs of factors of any number up to 100.

Name ______________________ Date ______________________

49 18 2 9

27 60 21

7 8 35

28 64 40

100 32 36

4 5

6 25 81

63 3 16

⑨ Change to decimals

$\frac{A}{10}$ $\frac{1}{4}$ $\frac{1}{2}$ $3\frac{E}{to4}$ $\frac{3}{4}$ to 10

⑩ order decimals.

0.25 0.4 0.5 $\overset{0.3}{}$ 0.75

Ys 05/06

... system

... r (e.g. change $\frac{13}{10}$ to $1\frac{3}{10}$).

...alent, including relating hundredths to tenths

...$\frac{1}{2}$ and position them on a number line.

Resources

Provide each child with the following:
- a copy of Activity 6 ...
- a red, blue, green and yellow coloured pencil
- a pencil

Key words

fraction equivalent equivalence one half one third
one quarter one fifth improper fraction mixed number order

Say to the children:

Listen carefully.

I am going to tell you some things to do.

I will say them only once, so listen very carefully.

Do only the things you are told to do and nothing else.

If you make a mistake, cross it out. Do not use an eraser.

There are 13 parts to this activity.

The activity

1. Look at the grid at the top of the sheet. Find one half and colour it red.

2. Now find all the other fractions that are equivalent to one half and colour them red.

3. Find one third and colour it blue.

4. Now find all the other fractions that are equivalent to one third and colour them blue.

5. Find one quarter and colour it green.

6. Now find all the other fractions that are equivalent to one quarter and colour them green.

7. Find one fifth and colour it yellow.

8. Now find all the other fractions that are equivalent to one fifth and colour them yellow.

9. Look at the fractions underneath the grid. All these fractions are improper fractions. Change each improper fraction to a mixed number. Write the answers in the circles.

10. Look at the mixed numbers you have just written in the circles. Put these mixed numbers in order on the number line, starting with the smallest. Write them in the boxes under the number line.

11. Look at the fractions next to the star. Which of these fractions are less than one half? Colour these fractions red.

12. Write your name inside the star.

13. Look at the fractions next to the smiling face. Mark each of these fractions on the number line.

Answers

Discussion questions

↓ Tell me a fraction that is equivalent to one half/one quarter/one third/one fifth.

↓ Read me a fraction on the grid.

■ Look at the grid. Which fractions are equivalent to one third? ($\frac{2}{6}$, $\frac{5}{15}$, $\frac{4}{12}$, $\frac{7}{21}$)

■ What is $\frac{16}{10}$ as a mixed number? ($1\frac{6}{10}$ or $1\frac{3}{5}$)

↑ Look at the numbers next to the smiling face. Tell me these fractions in order, starting with the smallest. (0, $\frac{1}{10}$, $\frac{3}{10}$, $\frac{2}{5}$, $\frac{1}{2}$, $\frac{14}{20}$, $\frac{3}{4}$, $\frac{4}{5}$, 1)

↑ Look at the fractions next to the star. Which fractions are greater than one half? ($\frac{70}{100}$, $\frac{7}{10}$, $\frac{12}{20}$)

Fractions, decimals and percentages

- Change an improper fraction to a mixed number (e.g. change $\frac{13}{10}$ to $1\frac{3}{10}$).
- Recognise when two simple fractions are equivalent, including relating hundredths to tenths (e.g. $\frac{70}{100} = \frac{7}{10}$).
- Order a set of fractions such as 2, $2\frac{3}{4}$, $1\frac{3}{4}$, $2\frac{1}{2}$, $1\frac{1}{2}$ and position them on a number line.

Date _____

$\frac{1}{2}$	$\frac{5}{15}$	$\frac{6}{12}$	$\frac{2}{10}$	$\frac{1}{3}$
$\frac{1}{4}$	$\frac{6}{24}$	$\frac{4}{20}$	$\frac{2}{4}$	$\frac{2}{8}$
$\frac{10}{50}$	$\frac{3}{6}$	$\frac{25}{100}$	$\frac{6}{30}$	$\frac{7}{21}$
$\frac{2}{6}$	$\frac{1}{5}$	$\frac{4}{12}$	$\frac{10}{40}$	$\frac{4}{8}$

$\frac{14}{10}$ → ◯ $\frac{36}{10}$ → ◯ $\frac{24}{10}$ → ◯ $\frac{16}{10}$ → ◯ $\frac{23}{10}$ → ◯

★ $\frac{1}{10}$ $\frac{1}{20}$ $\frac{70}{100}$ $\frac{2}{5}$ $\frac{7}{10}$ $\frac{12}{20}$

$\frac{3}{4}$ $\frac{2}{5}$ $\frac{1}{10}$ $\frac{4}{5}$ $\frac{1}{2}$ $\frac{14}{20}$ $\frac{3}{10}$

0 ———————————————————————— 1

Activity 7

Year 5 Numbers and the number system

Fractions, decimals and percentages

■ Relate fractions to division, and use division to find simple fractions, including tenths and hundredths, of numbers and quantities (e.g. $\frac{3}{4}$ of 12, $\frac{1}{10}$ of 50, $\frac{1}{100}$ of £3).

Resources

Provide each child with the following:
■ a copy of Activity 7 pupil sheet
■ a red, blue, green and yellow coloured pencil

Key words

zero, one, two…one thousand   one half   one quarter
three quarters   one third   one fifth   one tenth   one hundredth

Say to the children:

Listen carefully.

I am going to tell you some things to do.

I will say them only once, so listen very carefully.

Do only the things you are told to do and nothing else.

If you make a mistake, cross it out. Do not use an eraser.

There are 17 parts to this activity.

The activity

1. Look at Grid A. Find the number 40 and colour it red. What is one fifth of 40? Find the answer in Grid B and colour it red.

2. Look at Grid A. Find the number 15 and colour it red. What is one third of 15? Find the answer in Grid B and colour it red.

3. Look at Grid A. Find the number 240 and colour it blue. What is one tenth of 240? Find the answer in Grid B and colour it blue.

4. Look at Grid A. Find the number 700 and colour it blue. What is one hundredth of 700? Find the answer in Grid B and colour it blue.

5. Look at Grid A. Find the number 36 and colour it green. What is one half of 36? Find the answer in Grid B and colour it green.

6. Look at Grid A. Find the number 50 and colour it green. What is one fifth of 50? Find the answer in Grid B and colour it green.

7. Look at Grid A. Find the number 20 and colour it yellow. What is three tenths of 20? Find the answer in Grid B and colour it yellow.

8. Look at Grid A. Find the number eight and colour it yellow. What is one quarter of eight? Find the answer in Grid B and colour it yellow.

9. Look at Grid A. Find the number 100 and colour it red. What is nine tenths of 100? Find the answer in Grid B and colour it red.

10. Look at Grid A. Find the number 400 and colour it blue. What is three quarters of 400? Find the answer in Grid B and colour it blue.

11. Look at Grid A. Find the number 90 and colour it green. What is seven tenths of 90? Find the answer in Grid B and colour it green.

12. Look at Grid A. Find the number 70 and colour it yellow. What is one half of 70? Find the answer in Grid B and colour it yellow.

13. Look at Grid A. Find the number 16 and colour it red. What is three quarters of 16? Find the answer in Grid B and colour it red.

14. Look at Grid A. Find the number 80 and colour it blue. What is two tenths of 80? Find the answer in Grid B and colour it blue.

15. Look at Grid A. Find the number 600 and colour it green. What is one quarter of 600? Find the answer in Grid B and colour it green.

16. Look at Grid A. Find the number 60 and colour it yellow. What is one third of 60? Find the answer in Grid B and colour it yellow.

17. Write your name at the bottom of the sheet.

Answers

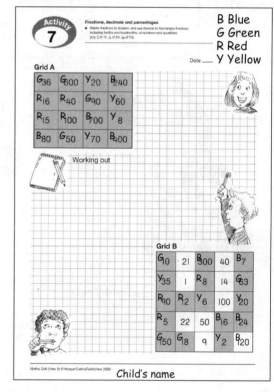

Discussion questions

↓ Look at Grid B. Tell me a number you coloured red. (5, 8, 12, 90)

↓ Look at Grid B. What colour is the number 150? (green)

■ Look at your working out. Tell me how you worked out one of the answers.

■ What is nine tenths of 100? (90)

↑ What is three quarters of 16? (12) How did you work it out? Did anyone work it out using a different method?

↑ What is one tenth/one hundredth of 700? (70/7)

Fractions, decimals and percentages

■ Relate fractions to division, and use division to find simple fractions, including tenths and hundredths, of numbers and quantities (e.g. $\frac{3}{4}$ of 12, $\frac{1}{10}$ of 50, $\frac{1}{100}$ of £3).

Date _____

Grid A

36	600	20	240
16	40	90	60
15	100	700	8
80	50	70	400

Working out

Grid B

10	21	300	40	7
35	1	8	14	63
90	12	6	100	20
5	22	50	16	24
150	18	9	2	120

Fractions, decimals and percentages

- Know what each digit represents in a number with up to two decimal places.
- Order a set of numbers or measurements with the same number of decimal places.
- Round a number with one or two decimal places to the nearest integer.

Resources

Provide each child with the following:
- a copy of Activity 8 pupil sheet
- a pencil

Key words

tenth hundredth nearest order round rounded to decimal place point worth represent decimal fraction equivalent equivalence smallest largest

Say to the children:

Listen carefully.

I am going to tell you some things to do.

I will say them only once, so listen very carefully.

Do only the things you are told to do and nothing else.

If you make a mistake, cross it out. Do not use an eraser.

There are 16 parts to this activity.

The activity

1. What does the digit three in 4.38 represent? Write the answer in box three.

2. What is the four worth in the number 5.24? Write the answer in box four.

3. Look at the measurements at the top of the sheet. Put these lengths in order, largest first. Write the answer in box one.

4. What is the decimal fraction equivalent to three tenths and seven hundredths? Write the answer in box six.

5. What is the decimal fraction equivalent to forty-one hundredths? Write the answer in box eight.

6. What is the decimal fraction equivalent to eight and nine hundredths? Write the answer in box ten.

7. Write your name in box 14.

8. What is 8.7 rounded to the nearest whole number? Write the answer in box five.

9. Look at the decimals at the top of the sheet. Put these decimals in order, smallest first. Write the answer in box 15.

10. What is 13 pounds 26 pence rounded to the nearest pound? Write the answer in box 11.

11. Look at the money at the bottom of the sheet. Put these amounts in order, largest first. Write the answer in box two.

12. What is 2.5 metres rounded to the nearest metre? Write the answer in box seven.

13. What is the decimal fraction equivalent to eight and one tenth? Write the answer in box 13.

14. What is 128.4 rounded to the nearest whole number? Write the answer in box nine.

15. What does the digit five in 14.85 represent? Write the answer in box 12.

16. Look at the decimals at the bottom of the sheet. Put these decimals in order, smallest first. Write the answer in box 16.

Answers

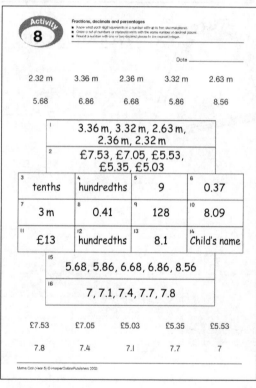

Discussion questions

↓ What did you write in box five? (9)

↓ Where did you write 8.1? (box 13)

■ What did you write in box one? (3.36 m, 3.32 m, 2.63 m, 2.36 m, 2.32 m)

■ What is the decimal fraction equivalent to eight and nine hundredths? (8.09)

↑ What is 13 pounds 26 pence rounded to the nearest pound/ten pence? (£13/£13.30)

↑ Look at the decimals at the top of the sheet. What does the eight represent in each of these decimals? (5.68 – hundredths, 6.86 – tenths, 6.68 – hundredths, 5.86 – tenths, 8.56 – ones or units)

Fractions, decimals and percentages

- Know what each digit represents in a number with up to two decimal places.
- Order a set of numbers or measurements with the same number of decimal places.
- Round a number with one or two decimal places to the nearest integer.

Date _____

2.32 m	3.36 m	2.36 m	3.32 m	2.63 m
5.68	6.86	6.68	5.86	8.56

1			
2			

3	4	5	6
7	8	9	10
11	12	13	14

15			
16			

£7.53	£7.05	£5.03	£5.35	£5.53
7.8	7.4	7.1	7.7	7

Year 5 Numbers and the number system

Fractions, decimals and percentages

■ Relate fractions to their decimal representations: that is, recognise the equivalence between the decimal and fraction forms of one half, one quarter, three quarters… and tenths and hundredths (e.g. $\frac{7}{10} = 0.7$, $\frac{27}{100} = 0.27$).

Resources

Provide each child with the following:
■ a copy of Activity 9 pupil sheet
■ a red, blue, green and yellow coloured pencil

Key words

zero, one, two…one thousand   one half   one quarter   three quarters   decimal   point   tenth   hundredth   equivalent   equivalence

Say to the children:

Listen carefully.

I am going to tell you some things to do.

I will say them only once, so listen very carefully.

Do only the things you are told to do and nothing else.

If you make a mistake, cross it out. Do not use an eraser.

There are 16 parts to this activity.

The activity

1. Look at the fractions in Grid A. Find seventeen hundredths and colour it red. Now find the decimal equivalent in Grid B and colour it red.

2. Look at the decimals in Grid B. Find 148.3 and colour it red. Now find the fraction equivalent in Grid A and colour it red.

3. Look at the decimals in Grid B. Find 3.45 and colour it blue. Now find the fraction equivalent in Grid A and colour it blue.

4. Look at the fractions in Grid A. Find twenty-six hundredths and colour it blue. Now find the decimal equivalent in Grid B and colour it blue.

5. Look at the fractions in Grid A. Find one half and colour it green. Now find the decimal equivalent in Grid B and colour it green.

6. Look at the decimals in Grid B. Find 0.25 and colour it green. Now find the fraction equivalent in Grid A and colour it green.

7. Look at the decimals in Grid B. Find 6.3 and colour it yellow. Now find the fraction equivalent in Grid A and colour it yellow.

8. Look at the fractions in Grid A. Find four and three quarters and colour it yellow. Now find the decimal equivalent in Grid B and colour it yellow.

9. Look at the fractions in Grid A. Find one tenth and colour it red. Now find the decimal equivalent in Grid B and colour it red.

10. Look at the decimals in Grid B. Find 0.2 and colour it blue. Now find the fraction equivalent in Grid A and colour it blue.

11. Look at the decimals in Grid B. Find 0.01 and colour it green. Now find the fraction equivalent in Grid A and colour it green.

12. Look at the fractions in Grid A. Find three quarters and colour it yellow. Now find the decimal equivalent in Grid B and colour it yellow.

13. Look at the decimals in Grid B. Find 2.6 and colour it red. Now find the fraction equivalent in Grid A and colour it red.

14. Look at the fractions in Grid A. Find three hundredths and colour it blue. Now find the decimal equivalent in Grid B and colour it blue.

15. Look at the decimals in Grid B. Find 1.5 and colour it green. Now find the fraction equivalent in Grid A and colour it green.

16. Write your name in the box at the bottom of the sheet.

Answers

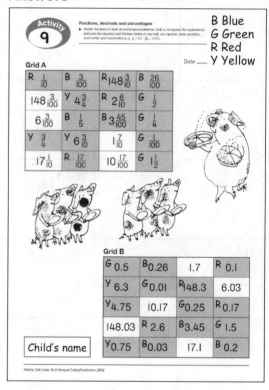

Discussion questions

↓ Look at Grid A. Tell me a fraction you coloured green. ($\frac{1}{100}$, $\frac{1}{4}$, $\frac{1}{2}$, $1\frac{1}{2}$)

↓ What is one half as a decimal? (0.5)

■ Look at Grid B. Which decimals did you colour red? (0.1, 0.17, 2.6, 148.3)

■ What is 148.03 as a mixed number? ($148\frac{3}{100}$)

↑ Look at both the grids. Choose a fraction and tell me its decimal equivalent.

↑ Look at one of the numbers you did not colour and tell me its decimal or fraction equivalent.

Activity 9

Fractions, decimals and percentages

■ Relate fractions to their decimal representations: that is, recognise the equivalence between the decimal and fraction forms of one half, one quarter, three quarters… and tenths and hundredths (e.g. $\frac{7}{10} = 0.7$, $\frac{27}{100} = 0.27$).

Date _____

Grid A

$\frac{1}{10}$	$\frac{3}{100}$	$148\frac{3}{10}$	$\frac{26}{100}$
$148\frac{3}{100}$	$4\frac{3}{4}$	$2\frac{6}{10}$	$\frac{1}{2}$
$6\frac{3}{100}$	$\frac{1}{5}$	$3\frac{45}{100}$	$\frac{1}{4}$
$\frac{3}{4}$	$6\frac{3}{10}$	$1\frac{7}{10}$	$\frac{1}{100}$
$17\frac{1}{10}$	$\frac{17}{100}$	$10\frac{17}{100}$	$1\frac{1}{2}$

Grid B

0.5	0.26	1.7	0.1
6.3	0.01	148.3	6.03
4.75	10.17	0.25	0.17
148.03	2.6	3.45	1.5
0.75	0.03	17.1	0.2

Fractions, decimals and percentages

■ Begin to understand percentage as the number of parts in every 100, and find simple percentages of small whole-number quantities (e.g. 25% of 8).

Resources

Provide each child with the following:
■ a copy of Activity 10 pupil sheet
■ a pencil
■ a coloured pencil

Key words

zero, one, two…one thousand　per cent　percentage

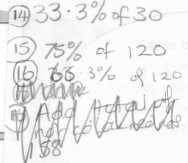

...e children:
...carefully.
...ou some things to do.
...ce, so listen very carefully.
...e told to do and nothing else.
...ss it out. Do not use an eraser.
...arts to this activity.

The activity

1. Find the jewel with the number 18 on it. What is 50 per cent of 18? Find the answer on the grid at the bottom of the sheet and colour that number.

2. Find the jewel with the number 16 on it. What is 75 per cent of 16? Find the answer on the grid at the bottom of the sheet and colour that number.

3. Find the jewel with the number 30 on it. What is 10 per cent of 30? Find the answer on the grid at the bottom of the sheet and colour that number.

4. Find the jewel with the number 32 on it. What is 25 per cent of 32? Find the answer on the grid at the bottom of the sheet and colour that number.

5. Find the jewel with the number 70 on it. What is 10 per cent of 70? Find the answer on the grid at the bottom of the sheet and colour that number.

6. Find the jewel with the number 120 on it. What is 50 per cent of 120? Find the answer on the grid at the bottom of the sheet and colour that number.

7. Find the jewel with the number 140 on it. What is 10 per cent of 140? Find the answer on the grid at the bottom of the sheet and colour that number.

8. Find the jewel with the number 160 on it. What is 25 per cent of 160? Find the answer on the grid at the bottom of the sheet and colour that number.

9. Find the jewel with the number 50 on it. What is 30 per cent of 50? Find the answer on the grid at the bottom of the sheet and colour that number.

10. Find the jewel with the number 40 on it. What is 75 per cent of 40? Find the answer on the grid at the bottom of the sheet and colour that number.

11. Find the jewel with the number 100 on it. What is 20 per cent of 100? Find the answer on the grid at the bottom of the sheet and colour that number.

12. Find the jewel with the number 200 on it. What is 75 per cent of 200? Find the answer on the grid at the bottom of the sheet and colour that number.

13. Find the jewel with the number 170 on it. What is 50 per cent of 170? Find the answer on the grid at the bottom of the sheet and colour that number.

14. Write your name above the words 'Working out'.

Answers

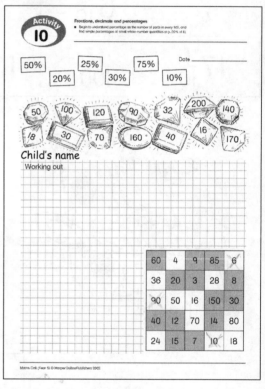

Discussion questions

↓ Tell me one of the numbers you coloured on the grid?

↓ What numbers did you not colour on the grid. (4, 6, 10, 16, 18, 24, 28, 36, 50, 70, 80, 90)

■ What is 25 per cent of 160? (40)

■ What is 25/50/75 per cent of 120? (30/60/90) How did you work it out?

↑ Make a calculation using a percentage from the top of the sheet and one of the numbers on the jewels. What is the answer?

↑ What is 80 per cent of 30? (24) So what is 10/20/30/40/50/60/70/90 per cent of 30? (3/6/9/12/15/18/21/27) How did you work these out? What do you notice?

Fractions, decimals and percentages

■ Begin to understand percentage as the number of parts in every 100, and find simple percentages of small whole-number quantities (e.g. 25% of 8).

Date _____

50%   25%   75%

20%   30%   10%

50   100   120   90   32   200   140

18   30   70   160   40   16   170

Working out

60	4	9	85	6
36	20	3	28	8
90	50	16	150	30
40	12	70	14	80
24	15	7	10	18

Addition and subtraction

■ Derive quickly or continue to derive quickly:
  – decimals that total 1 (e.g. 0.2 + 0.8) or 10 (e.g. 6.2 + 3.8);
  – all two-digit pairs that total 100 (e.g. 43 + 57);
  – all pairs of multiples of 50 with a total of 1000 (e.g. 350 + 650).

Resources

Provide each child with the following:
■ a copy of Activity 11 pupil sheet
■ a red, blue, green, yellow and orange coloured pencil

Key words

zero, one, two…one thousand   decimal   point   total
equal   total

Say to the children:

Listen carefully.

I am going to tell you some things to do.

I will say them only once, so listen very carefully.

Do only the things you are told to do and nothing else.

If you make a mistake, cross it out. Do not use an eraser.

There are 17 parts to this activity.

The activity

1. Find 0.2 and colour it red. 0.2 and what other decimal total one? Find that decimal and colour it red.

2. Find 7.3 and colour it red. 7.3 and what other decimal total 10? Find that decimal and colour it red.

3. Find 350 and colour it blue. 350 and what other number total 1000? Find that number and colour it blue.

4. Find 1.5 and colour it blue. 1.5 and what other decimal equal 10? Find that decimal and colour it blue.

5. Find 43 and colour it green. 43 and what other number equal 100? Find that number and colour it green.

6. Find 150 and colour it green. 150 and what other number total 1000? Find that number and colour it green.

7. Find 0.1 and colour it yellow. 0.1 and what other decimal total one? Find that decimal and colour it yellow.

8. Find 12 and colour it yellow. 12 and what other number equal 100? Find that number and colour it yellow.

9. Find 6.2 and colour it orange. 6.2 and what other decimal total 10? Find that decimal and colour it orange.

10. Find 450 and colour it orange. 450 and what other number equal 1000? Find that number and colour it orange.

11. Find 5.4 and draw a cross through the decimal. 5.4 and what other decimal total 10? Find that decimal and draw a cross through it.

12. Find 64 and colour it red. 64 and what other number total 100? Find that number and colour it red.

13. Find 0.4 and colour it blue. 0.4 and what other decimal equal one? Find that decimal and colour it blue.

14. Find 0.7 and colour it green. 0.7 and what other decimal equal one? Find that decimal and colour it green.

15. Find 750 and colour it yellow. 750 and what other number total 1000? Find that number and colour it yellow.

16. Find 35 and colour it orange. 35 and what other number equal 100? Find that number and colour it orange.

17. Find 79 and write your name under it. 79 and what other number equal 100? Find that number and write your name under it.

Answers

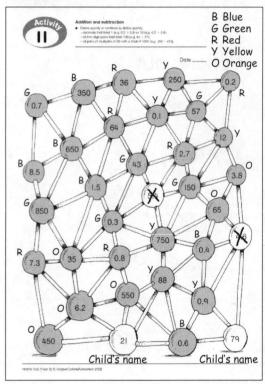

Discussion questions

↓ Look at your sheet and tell me any two numbers that total 100/1000?

↓ 850 and what other number total 1000? (150)

■ 1.5 and what other decimal total 10? (8.5)

■ Tell me any two numbers that equal 100.

↑ Tell me any two numbers that total 10/100/1000 that are not on the sheet.

↑ If 350 and 650 equal 1000, 3500 and what other number total 10 000? (6500)

Addition and subtraction

■ Derive quickly or continue to derive quickly:
   – decimals that total 1 (e.g. 0.2 + 0.8) or 10 (e.g. 6.2 + 3.8);
   – all two-digit pairs that total 100 (e.g. 43 + 57);
   – all pairs of multiples of 50 with a total of 1000 (e.g. 350 + 650).

Date _____

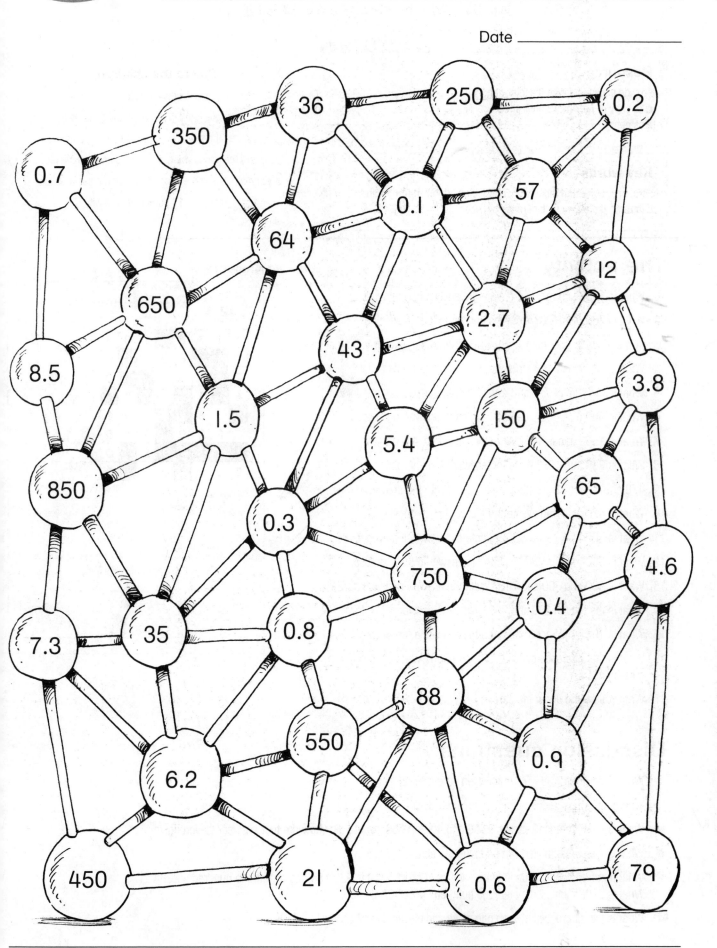

Year 5 Calculations

Addition and subtraction

■ Use known number facts and place value for mental addition and subtraction
(e.g. 470 + 380, 810 − 380, 7.4 + 9.8, 9.2 − 8.6).

Resources

Provide each child with the following:
■ a copy of Activity 12 pupil sheet
■ a pencil

Key words

zero, one, two…ten thousand   add   plus   total   sum   minus
subtract   take away   difference between

Say to the children:

Listen carefully.

I am going to tell you some things to do.

I will say them only once, so listen very carefully.

Do only the things you are told to do and nothing else.

If you make a mistake, cross it out. Do not use an eraser.

There are 17 parts to this activity.

The activity

1. What is 1638 subtract 500? Write the answer in one across.

2. What is 260 plus 170? Write the answer in four down.

3. 464 and what other number total 500? Write the answer in nine across.

4. What is 384 plus 210? Write the answer in eight down.

5. What is the sum of 776 and 400? Write the answer in one down.

6. What is 900 plus 600 plus 700? Write the answer in twelve across.

7. What is 1560 minus 400? Write the answer in seven down.

8. What is 238 add 420? Write the answer in five across.

9. 478 and what other number equal 500? Write the answer in fourteen across.

10. What is 470 plus 390? Write the answer in two down.

11. What is 3004 take away 2902? Write the answer in seven across.

12. What is 5003 minus 4899? Write the answer in three across.

13. What is 500 add 300 add 700? Write the answer in eleven down.

14. What is the total of 230 and 296? Write the answer in six down.

15. What is 1982 subtract 600? Write the answer in ten down.

16. What is the difference between 940 and 360? Write the answer in thirteen across.

17. Write your name under the date.

Answers

Discussion questions

↓ What number did you write in fourteen across? (22)

↓ Where did you write the number 430? (four down)

■ What is the difference between 1560 and 400? (1160) Where did you write that answer? (seven down)

■ What is the sum of nine down and fourteen across? (54)

↑ What number did you write in twelve across? (2200) What is 2200 divided by ten/one hundred? (220/22)
What is 2200 multiplied by ten/one hundred? (22 000/220 000)

↑ What is the difference between one down and eleven down? (324)

Activity 12

Addition and subtraction

■ Use known number facts and place value for mental addition and
subtraction (e.g. 470 + 380, 810 − 380, 7.4 + 9.8, 9.2 − 8.6).

Date _____

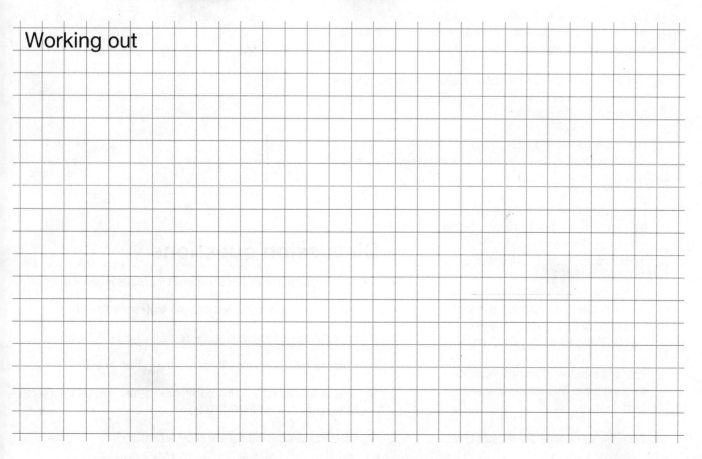

Working out

Year 5 Calculations

Addition and subtraction

- Use informal pencil and paper methods to support, record or explain additions and subtractions.
- Extend written methods to column addition/subtraction of two integers less than 10 000.

Resources

Provide each child with the following:
- a copy of Activity 13 pupil sheet
- a pencil
- a calculator (optional)

Key words

zero, one, two…ten thousand   calculation   addition   subtraction   sign   integer

Say to the children:

Listen carefully.

I am going to tell you some things to do.

I will say them only once, so listen very carefully.

Do only the things you are told to do and nothing else.

If you make a mistake, cross it out. Do not use an eraser.

There are 10 parts to this activity.

The activity

1. Find the number 1549. Write an addition sign in the box. Now answer the calculation.

2. Look at the answer to the calculation you have just done. Find that number in another calculation. Write a subtraction sign in the box. Now answer the calculation.

3. Look at the answer to the calculation you have just done. Find that number in another calculation. Write a subtraction sign in the box. Now answer the calculation.

4. Look at the answer to the calculation you have just done. Find that number in another calculation. Write a subtraction sign in the box. Now answer the calculation.

5. Look at the answer to the calculation you have just done. Find that number in another calculation. Write an addition sign in the box. Now answer the calculation.

6. Look at the answer to the calculation you have just done. Find that number in another calculation. Write an addition sign in the box. Now answer the calculation.

7. Look at the answer to the calculation you have just done. Find that number in another calculation. Write a subtraction sign in the box. Now answer the calculation.

8. Look at the answer to the calculation you have just done. Find that number in another calculation. Write a subtraction sign in the box. Now answer the calculation.

9. Look at the answer to the calculation you have just done. Write that number in the treasure chest.

10. Write your name under the treasure chest.

Answers

Discussion questions

↓ What is the answer to the calculation in the top left-hand corner? (8772)

↓ Tell me the answer to a calculation you know the answer to.

■ What number did you write inside the treasure chest? (1868)

■ Choose a calculation and tell me how you worked it out?

↑ Look at the calculation in the top left-hand corner. What is the difference between 4923 and 3849? (1074)

↑ Which calculations did you find easy/hard? Why?

Addition and subtraction
- Use informal pencil and paper methods to support, record or explain additions and subtractions.
- Extend written methods to column addition/subtraction of two integers less than 10 000.

Date _____

```
  4 9 2 3        2 0 2 2        6 8 0 5
☐ 3 8 4 9      ☐   3 8 4      ☐ 4 9 3 7


  8 7 7 2        1 6 3 8        8 3 2
☐ 1 9 6 7      ☐   8 0 6      ☐ 5 0 5


  1 5 4 9          3 2 7
☐   4 7 3      ☐ 4 5 9 6
```

Year 5 Calculations

Addition and subtraction

- Use informal pencil and paper methods to support, record or explain additions and subtractions.
- Extend written methods to addition or subtraction of a pair of decimal fractions, both with one or both with two decimal places (e.g. £29.78 + £53.34).

Resources

Provide each child with the following:
- a copy of Activity 14 pupil sheet
- a pencil
- a calculator (optional)

Key words

zero, one, two…one hundred   decimal place   point
largest   smallest   first   second   last   add   subtract
difference between   total

Say to the children:

Listen carefully.

I am going to tell you some things to do.

I will say them only once, so listen very carefully.

Do only the things you are told to do and nothing else.

If you make a mistake, cross it out. Do not use an eraser.

There are 7 parts to this activity.

The activity

1. Look at row A. Add the smallest number to the largest number. Write the answer in box one.

2. Look at row A again. Subtract the last number from the first number. Write the answer in box two.

3. Look at row B. Add the first number to the last number. Write the answer in box three.

4. Look at row B again. Find the difference between the smallest number and the largest number. Write the answer in box four.

5. Look at row C. Find the total of the first and second numbers. Write the answer in box five.

6. Look at row C again. Take the last number away from the first number. Write the answer in box six.

7. Look at the six answers you have written down. Write your name below the smallest number.

Answers

A	23.6	41.7	12.8
B	2.87	8.73	4.65
C	27.36	12.97	15.79

Working out

1. 54.5

2. 10.8

3. 7.52

4. 5.86   Child's name

5. 40.33

6. 11.57

Discussion questions

↓ What number did you write in box one? (54.5)

↓ Look at your working out. Choose a calculation and explain how you worked it out.

■ Where did you write your name? (under 5.86) Why? (smallest number)

■ Look at row B. You were asked to add the first number to the last number. What is the answer? (7.52) How did you work it out? Did anyone work it out differently?

↑ What numbers did you write in boxes two and five? (10.8 and 40.33) What is the total of these two numbers? (51.13) What is the difference between these two numbers? (29.53)

↑ Look at all the numbers in rows A, B and C. Choose any two numbers and add them together. What is their difference?

Addition and subtraction

■ Use informal pencil and paper methods to support, record or explain additions and subtractions.

■ Extend written methods to addition or subtraction of a pair of decimal fractions, both with one or both with two decimal places (e.g. £29.78 + £53.34).

Date _____

A	23.6	41.7	12.8
B	2.87	8.73	4.65
C	27.36	12.97	15.79

Working out

1

2

3

4

5

6

Addition

- Use informal pencil and paper methods to support, record or explain additions.
- Extend written methods to addition of more than two integers less than 10 000.

Resources

Provide each child with the following:
- a copy of Activity 15 pupil sheet
- a pencil
- a calculator (optional)

Key words

zero, one, two...ten thousand   add   first   second   third
fourth   integer

Say to the children:

Listen carefully.

I am going to tell you some things to do.

I will say them only once, so listen very carefully.

Do only the things you are told to do and nothing else.

If you make a mistake, cross it out. Do not use an eraser.

There are 7 parts to this activity.

The activity

1. Look at the numbers on the first column of the Greek temple. Draw rings around the numbers 3642, 683 and 2409. Add these three numbers together and write the answer in box one.

2. Look at the numbers on the second column of the Greek temple. Draw rings around the numbers 732, 851 and 4062. Add these three numbers together and write the answer in box two.

3. Look at the numbers on the third column of the Greek temple. Draw rings around the numbers 596, 9303 and 348. Add these three numbers together and write the answer in box three.

4. Look at the numbers on the fourth column of the Greek temple. Draw rings around the numbers 2470, 413 and 901. Add these three numbers together and write the answer in box four.

   Add too   5 894 7 509 1043   8515

5. Look at the four numbers you have not drawn a ring around. Add these four numbers together and write the answer in box five.

6. Look at the four numbers at the bottom of each column. Add these four numbers together and write the answer in box six.

7. Look at the six answers you have written down. Write your name under the largest number.

Answers

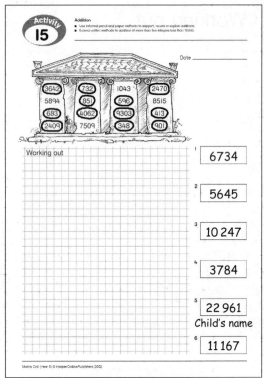

① 12,628
② 13,154
③ 11,290
④ 12,399

Discussion questions

↓ Under which box did you write your name? (5) What number is in box 5? (22 961)

↓ Where did you write the number 3784? (box 4)

■ What number did you write in box one? (6734)

■ Look at the six answers you have written down. Round each number to the nearest ten/hundred/thousand. (6734 – 6730/6700/7000; 5645 – 5650/5600/6000; 10 247 – 10 250/10 200/10 000; 3784 – 3780/3800/4000; 22 961 – 22 960/23 000/23 000; 11 167 – 11 170/11 200/11 000)

↑ Tell me the answer to a calculation you know? How did you work it out?

↑ Look at the four numbers at the bottom of each column. What is the sum of these four numbers? (11 167) Where did you write that answer? (box 6)

Addition

- Use informal pencil and paper methods to support, record or explain additions.
- Extend written methods to addition of more than two integers less than 10 000.

Date _____

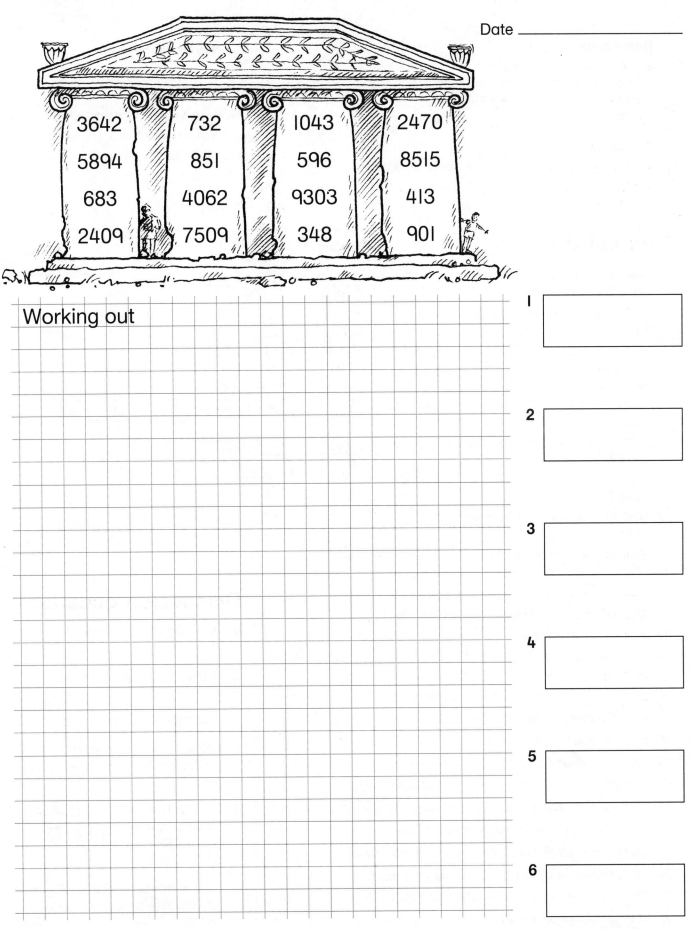

3642	732	1043	2470
5894	851	596	8515
683	4062	9303	413
2409	7509	348	901

Working out

1 ☐

2 ☐

3 ☐

4 ☐

5 ☐

6 ☐

Activity 16

Multiplication

■ Know by heart all multiplication facts up to 10 × 10.

Resources

Provide each child with the following:
- ■ a copy of Activity 16 pupil sheet
- ■ a pencil
- ■ a coloured pencil

Key words

zero, one, two…one hundred groups of times multiplied by product of

Say to the children:

Listen carefully.

I am going to tell you some things to do.

I will say them only once, so listen very carefully.

Do only the things you are told to do and nothing else.

If you make a mistake, cross it out. Do not use an eraser.

There are 26 parts to this activity.

The activity

1. What is ten multiplied by six? Find that number and colour it.

2. What is eight times eight? Find that number and colour it.

3. What is two times six? Find that number and colour it.

4. What is five multiplied by three? Find that number and colour it.

5. What is seven times ten? Find that number and colour it.

6. What is six times seven? Find that number and colour it.

7. What are seven lots of seven? Find that number and colour it.

8. What is ten times nine? Find that number and colour it.

9. What is the product of eight and six? Find that number and colour it.

10. What is nine multiplied by six? Find that number and colour it.

11. What is five times five? Find that number and colour it.

12. What is eight multiplied by four? Find that number and colour it.

13. What are nine groups of nine? Find that number and colour it.

14. What is five times four? Find that number and colour it.

15. What is one lot of four? Find that number and colour it.

16. What is nine times eight? Find that number and colour it.

17. What is the product of four and six? Find that number and colour it.

18. What is three times ten? Find that number and colour it.

19. What is seven times five? Find that number and colour it.

20. What is the product of nine and three? Find that number and colour it.

21. What is seven multiplied by nine? Find that number and colour it.

22. What is three times two? Find that number and colour it.

23. What is seven multiplied by eight? Find that number and colour it.

24. What are seven lots of four? Find that number and colour it.

25. What is four times nine? Find that number and colour it.

26. Write your name above the date.

Answers

Discussion questions

↓ Which notes did you not colour?
(14 and 31)

↓ Tell me a multiplication table you know?

■ Do you know what this piece of music is called? (Brahms' Lullaby)

■ Choose one of the numbers on the sheet. What multiplication fact will give you that answer?

↑ What four facts can you make from the numbers seven, nine and sixty-three?
(7 × 9 = 63, 9 × 7 = 63, 63 ÷ 9 = 7, 63 ÷ 7 = 9)

↑ Which multiplication tables do you know very well? Which ones are you not so sure of?

(handwritten) 7 × 2 (at item 15)

(handwritten) under 2×2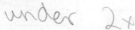

(handwritten) Factors of 14.
31 – what is?
prime no

Multiplication
- Know by heart all multiplication facts up to 10 × 10.

Date —

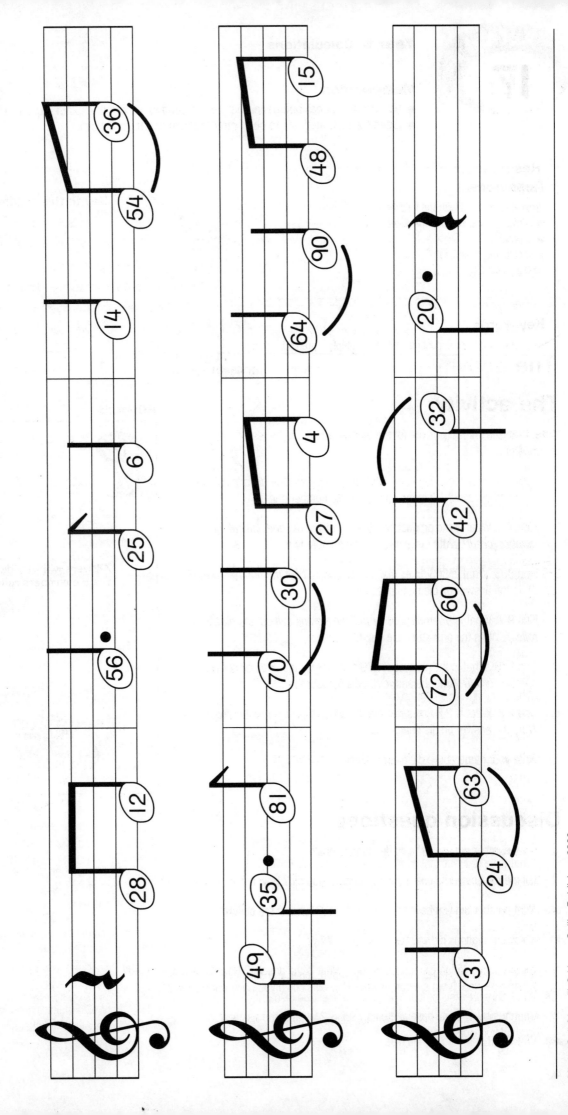

Multiplication

- Use informal pencil and paper methods to support, record or explain multiplications.
- Extend written methods to short multiplication of HTU or U.t by U.

Resources

Provide each child with the following:
- a copy of Activity 17 pupil sheet
- a pencil
- a calculator (optional)

You will also need a 0–9 die.

Key words

zero, one, two…ten thousand   point   multiply   product   times

Say to the children:

Listen carefully.

I am going to tell you some things to do.

I will say them only once, so listen very carefully.

Do only the things you are told to do and nothing else.

If you make a mistake, cross it out. Do not use an eraser.

There are 7 parts to this activity.

The activity

Note: Italicised instructions are for the teacher and not to be read out to the children.

1. Look at the spinners. Find 624. Multiply 624 by *(roll the die and call out the number rolled)*. Write the answer on die number one.

2. Find 7.5. What is the product of 7.5 and *(roll the die and call out the number rolled)*? Write the answer on die number two.

3. Find 803. What is 803 times *(roll the die and call out the number rolled)*? Write the answer on die number three.

4. Find 9.7. What is 9.7 multiplied by *(roll the die and call out the number rolled)*? Write the answer on die number four.

5. Find 379. What is the product of 379 and *(roll the die and call out the number rolled)*? Write the answer on die number five.

6. Find 2.8. What is 2.8 times *(roll the die and call out the number rolled)*? Write the answer on die number six.

7. Write your name above die number three.

Answers

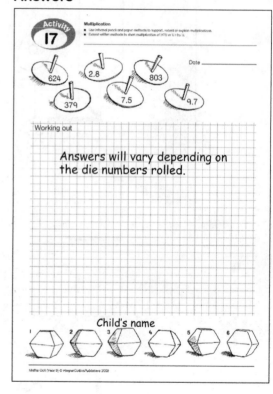

Discussion questions

↓ What number did you write on die number one?

↓ Tell me the answer to one of the calculations you did? How did you work it out?

■ What number did you have to multiply 803 by? What is the answer?

■ Which calculations did you find easy/hard? Why?

↑ Choose a calculation you have just done. What is the answer? How did you work it out?
Did anyone work it out a different way? How else could you have worked it out?

↑ What number did you have to multiply 9.7 by? What is the answer?
How did you work it out?

Multiplication

- Use informal pencil and paper methods to support, record or explain multiplications.
- Extend written methods to short multiplication of HTU or U.t by U.

Date _____

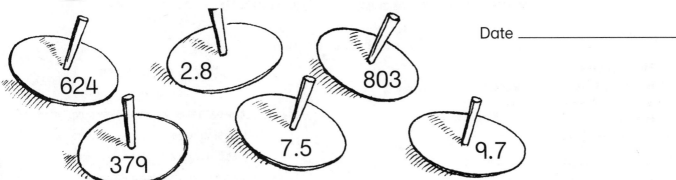

624   2.8   803   379   7.5   9.7

Working out

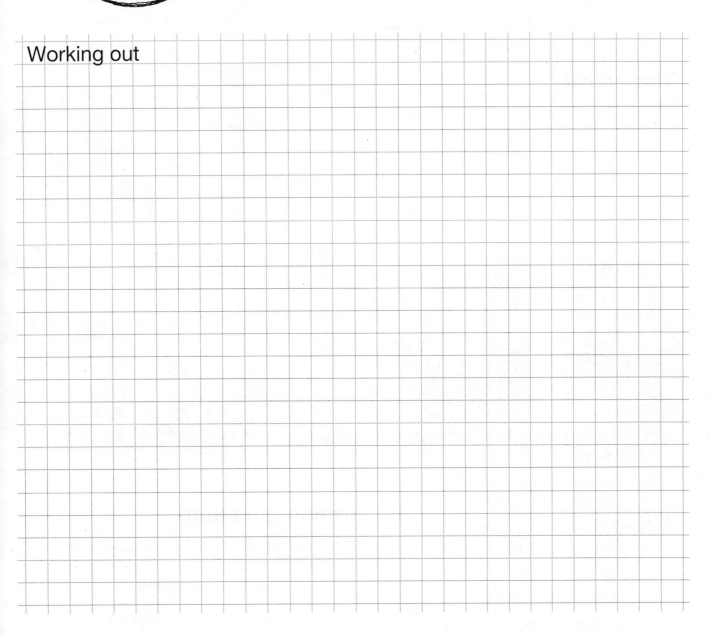

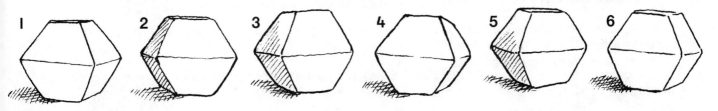

1   2   3   4   5   6

Year 5 Calculations

Multiplication

- Use informal pencil and paper methods to support, record or explain multiplications.
- Extend written methods to long multiplication of TU by TU.

Resources

Provide each child with the following:
- a copy of Activity 18 pupil sheet
- a pencil
- a calculator (optional)

Key words

zero, one, two…ten thousand   times   multiply   digit   add

Say to the children:

Listen carefully.

I am going to tell you some things to do.

I will say them only once, so listen very carefully.

Do only the things you are told to do and nothing else.

If you make a mistake, cross it out. Do not use an eraser.

There are 14 parts to this activity.

The activity

1. Look at the number cards. Find 47 and 58. Multiply these two numbers together.

2. Look at the rectangles at the bottom of the sheet. Write the answer in rectangle one. Make sure that you write each digit in a box of its own.

3. Look at the number cards. Find 32 and 74. Multiply these two numbers together.

4. Write the answer in rectangle two. Make sure that you write each digit in a box of its own.

5. Look at the number cards. Find 63 and 91. Multiply these two numbers together.

6. Write the answer in rectangle three. Make sure that you write each digit in a box of its own.

7. Look at the number cards. Find 77 and 34. Multiply these two numbers together.

8. Write the answer in rectangle four. Make sure that you write each digit in a box of its own.

9. Look at the number cards. Find 56 and 69. Multiply these two numbers together.

10. Write the answer in rectangle five. Make sure that you write each digit in a box of its own.

11. Look at the number cards. Find 85 and 28. Multiply these two numbers together.

12. Write the answer in rectangle six. Make sure that you write each digit in a box of its own.

13. Look at each of the digits that you have written in the grey boxes. Add these digits together and write the answer in the circle.

14. Write your name under the circle.

Answers

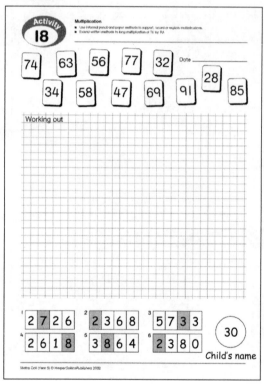

Discussion questions

↓ Look at the answers in the rectangles. What is the largest/smallest answer? (5733/2368)

↓ What number did you write in rectangle one? (2726)

■ What digits did you write in the grey boxes? (7, 2, 3, 8, 8, 2)

■ What number did you write in the circle? (30)

↑ Tell me the answer to a calculation you know the answer to. How did you work it out?

↑ Look at the answers in the rectangles. Which numbers are greater than 2500? (2726, 5733, 2618, 3864)

Multiplication

- Use informal pencil and paper methods to support, record or explain multiplications.
- Extend written methods to long multiplication of TU by TU.

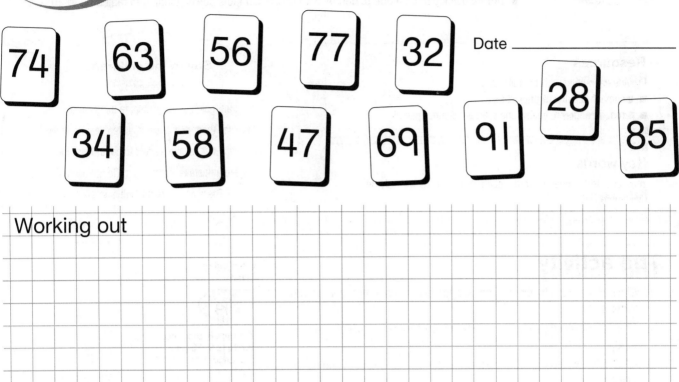

Date _____

Working out

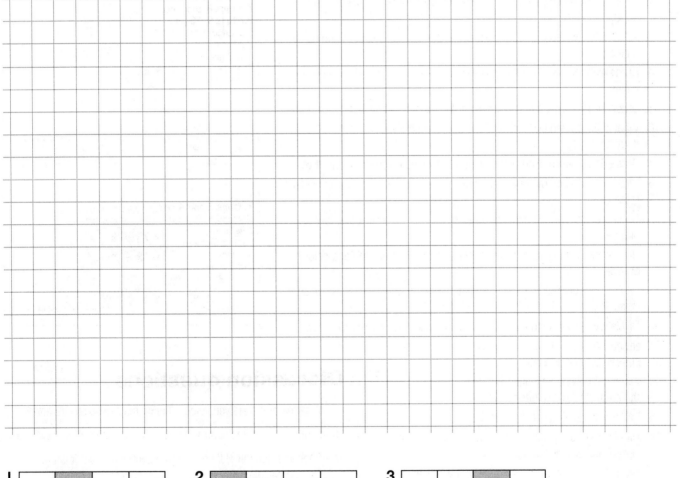

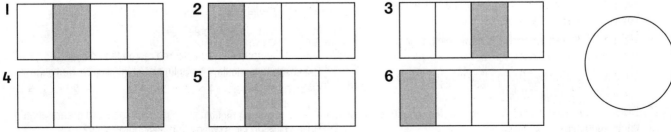

Activity 19

Division

■ Derive quickly or continue to derive quickly division facts corresponding to tables up to 10 × 10.

Resources

Provide each child with the following:
■ a copy of Activity 19 pupil sheet
■ a red, blue, green, yellow and orange coloured pencil

Key words

zero, one, two…one hundred   divided by   divide by   divide
divide into

Say to the children:

Listen carefully.

I am going to tell you some things to do.

I will say them only once, so listen very carefully.

Do only the things you are told to do and nothing else.

If you make a mistake, cross it out. Do not use an eraser.

There are 20 parts to this activity.

The activity

1. What is 24 divided by three? Find that number on the remote control and colour it red.

2. What is 56 divided by eight? Find that number on the calculator and colour it red.

3. What is 15 divided by five? Find that number on the calculator and colour it blue.

4. Divide eight by two. Find that number on the remote control and colour it blue.

5. Divide 36 by six. Find that number on the remote control and colour it green.

6. What is 20 divided by four? Find that number on the calculator and colour it green.

7. Divide 63 by seven. Find that number on the calculator and colour it yellow.

8. What is 18 divided by nine? Find that number on the calculator and colour it yellow.

9. Divide 10 into 100. Find that number on the remote control and colour it orange.

10. Divide three into 27. Find that number on the remote control and colour it orange.

11. What is four divided by four? Find that number on the remote control and colour it red.

12. Divide six into 24. Find that number on the calculator and colour it red.

13. Divide 14 by two. Find that number on the remote control and colour it blue.

14. What is 54 divided by nine? Find that number on the calculator and colour it blue.

15. Write your name above the calculator.

16. Divide five into 10. Find that number on the remote control and colour it green.

17. Divide 21 by seven. Find that number on the remote control and colour it green.

18. What is 64 divided by eight? Find that number on the calculator and colour it yellow.

19. What is 10 divided by 10? Find that number on the calculator and colour it yellow.

20. Divide 35 by seven. Find that number on the remote control and colour it orange.

Answers

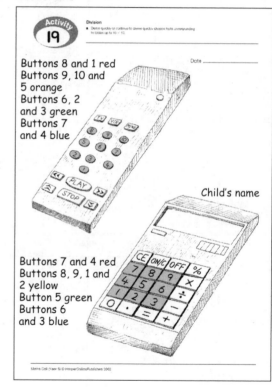

Activity 19 — Division

Buttons 8 and 1 red
Buttons 9, 10 and 5 orange
Buttons 6, 2 and 3 green
Buttons 7 and 4 blue

Date

Child's name

Buttons 7 and 4 red
Buttons 8, 9, 1 and 2 yellow
Button 5 green
Buttons 6 and 3 blue

Discussion questions

↓ What numbers did you colour blue on the calculator? (3 and 6)

↓ Look at the remote control. What colour is the number four? (blue)

■ Choose a number from the remote control and put it into a division calculation.

■ What is 27 divided by three? (9)

↑ Look at the numbers you coloured red on the calculator. Use these two numbers to make two multiplication and two division calculations. (4 × 7 = 28; 7 × 4 = 28; 28 ÷ 7 = 4; 28 ÷ 4 = 7)

↑ Which division facts do you find easy/hard? Why?

Division

■ Derive quickly or continue to derive quickly division facts corresponding to tables up to 10 × 10.

Date _____

Year 5 Calculations

Division

■ Use informal pencil and paper methods to support, record or explain divisions.
■ Extend written methods to short division of HTU by U (with integer remainder).

Resources

Provide each child with the following:
■ a copy of Activity 20 pupil sheet
■ a pencil
■ a calculator (optional)

You will also need a 0–9 die.

Key words

zero, one, two…ten thousand   divided by   divide

Say to the children:
Listen carefully.
I am going to tell you some things to do.
I will say them only once, so listen very carefully.
Do only the things you are told to do and nothing else.
If you make a mistake, cross it out. Do not use an eraser.
There are 7 parts to this activity.

The activity

Note: Italicised instructions are for the teacher and not to be read out to the children.

1. Look at the aeroplanes. Find 631. Divide 631 by *(roll the die and call out the number thrown)*. Write the answer on ship number one. 5

2. Find 863. What is 863 divided by *(roll the die and call out the number thrown)*? Write the answer on ship number two. 7

3. Find 374. Divide 374 by *(roll the die and call out the number thrown)*. 4 Write the answer on ship number three.

4. Find 549. What is 549 divided by *(roll the die and call out the number thrown)*? Write the answer on ship number four. 8 9

5. Find 785. Divide 785 by *(roll the die and call out the number thrown)*. Write the answer on ship number five. 3

6. Find 952. What is 952 divided by *(roll the die and call out the number thrown)*? Write the answer on ship number six. 8

7. Write your name above the ships.

Answers

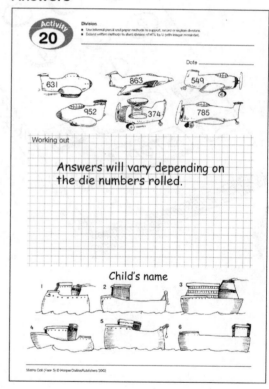

Discussion questions

↓ What number did you write on ship number three?

↓ Tell me the answer to one of the calculations you did? How did you work it out?

■ What number did you have to divide 374 by? What is the answer?

■ Which calculations did you find easy/hard? Why?

↑ Choose a calculation you have just done. What is the answer? How did you work it out? Did anyone work it out a different way? How else could you have worked it out?

↑ What do you need to know to work out the answers to these calculations? (multiplication tables) Which tables do you know well? Which tables are you not so sure about?

① 126 r 1
② 123 r 2
③ 93 r 2
④ 61
⑤ 261 r 2
⑥ 119
⑦ Smallest ÷ 0
1000 6.1

Division

■ Use informal pencil and paper methods to support, record or explain divisions.
■ Extend written methods to short division of HTU by U (with integer remainder).

Date _____

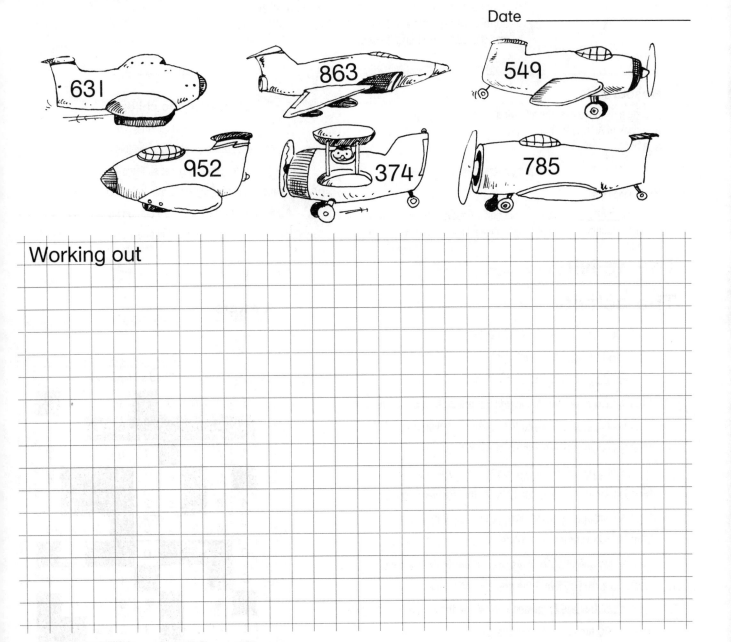

Working out

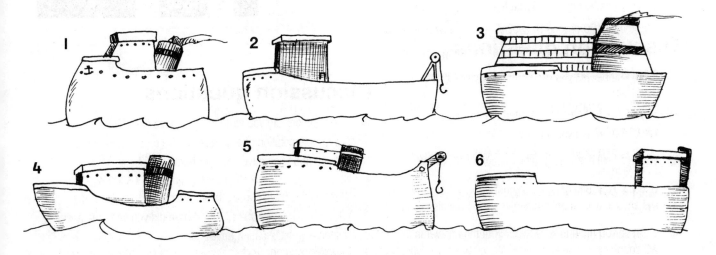

Year 5 Calculations

Multiplication and division

■ Derive quickly or continue to derive quickly:
- doubles of all whole numbers 1 to 100 (e.g. 78 × 2);
- doubles of multiples of 10 to 1000 (e.g. 670 × 2);
- doubles of multiples of 100 to 10000 (e.g. 6500 × 2);
- and the corresponding halves.

Resources

Provide each child with the following:
■ a copy of Activity 21 pupil sheet
■ a pencil

Key words

zero, one, two…one hundred thousand   double   twice   times
product   multiply   multiplied by   divided by   shared between
one half

Say to the children:

Listen carefully.

I am going to tell you some things to do.

I will say them only once, so listen very carefully.

Do only the things you are told to do and nothing else.

If you make a mistake, cross it out. Do not use an eraser.

There are 22 parts to this activity.

The activity

1. Write your name to the left of the date.

2. What is 60 multiplied by two? Write the answer in 17 across.

3. What is 160 times two? Write the answer in 18 across.

4. What is 12 800 divided by two? Write the answer in one across.

5. What is double 9600? Write the answer in seven down.

6. What is double 86? Write the answer in two across.

7. What is one half of 9400? Write the answer in nine down.

8. What is 940 multiplied by two? Write the answer in six down.

9. What is 68 divided by two? Write the answer in 13 across.

10. What is 35 000 times two? Write the answer in 10 across.

11. What is one half of 560? Write the answer in three down.

12. What is double 57? Write the answer in five across.

13. What is 5600 shared between two? Write the answer in 16 across.

14. What is 750 times two? Write the answer in 14 across.

15. What is one half of 190? Write the answer in 15 across.

16. What is 14 400 divided by two? Write the answer in 12 down.

17. What is 1300 divided by two? Write the answer in eight down.

18. What is 5300 times two? Write the answer in four down.

19. What is 8100 times two? Write the answer in seven across.

20. What is 740 shared between two? Write the answer in 11 across.

21. What is 460 divided by two? Write the answer in 16 down.

22. What is 460 multiplied by two? Write the answer in 15 down.

Answers

Discussion questions

↓ What number did you write in one across? (6400)

↓ Tell me the position of a number on the cross-number puzzle.

■ Did you find this activity easy or hard? Why?

■ What is double 750? (1500) What is half of 1500? (750) What do you notice about these numbers?

↑ What is half of 14 400? (7200) Where did you write the answer? (12 down)

↑ Choose a number from the cross-number puzzle and double/halve it.

Multiplication and division

■ Derive quickly or continue to derive quickly:
 – doubles of all whole numbers 1 to 100 (e.g. 78 × 2);
 – doubles of multiples of 10 to 1000 (e.g. 670 × 2);
 – doubles of multiples of 100 to 10000 (e.g. 6500 × 2);
 – and the corresponding halves.

Date _____

Activity 22

Year 5 Calculations

Multiplication and division
■ Use known facts and place value to multiply and divide mentally.

Resources
Provide each child with the following:
■ a copy of Activity 22 pupil sheet
■ a pencil

Key words
zero, one, two…one hundred thousand   times   multiplied by
lots of   groups of   product of   divided by   divided into
tenth   hundredth

Say to the children:
Listen carefully.
I am going to tell you some things to do.
I will say them only once, so listen very carefully.
Do only the things you are told to do and nothing else.
If you make a mistake, cross it out. Do not use an eraser.
There are 17 parts to this activity.

The activity

Look at the sheet. It shows a basketball court. This activity is like playing a game of basketball, but some of the rules are different. In our game there are sixteen players a side and there are lots of players defending the ring. Circles are Nowra and squares are Bomaderry. When a ball is passed from one player to another you draw a straight line. When a ball is dribbled from one player to another you draw a dotted line. When the ball goes to a number in a circle in the shaded part of Nowra's ring, it is a basket for Nowra. When the ball goes to a number in a square in the shaded part of Bomaderry's ring, it is a basket for Bomaderry. Each basket scores two points.

1. Place your pencil on the spot at the word Start.

2. Pass the ball to the answer to 6200 divided by 10.

3. 6200 divided by 10 passes the ball to 50 multiplied by 700. 50 multiplied by 700 dribbles the ball to 450 divided by two.

4. 450 divided by two passes the ball to 65 times four.

5. 65 times four passes the ball to the product of 700 and 5. The product of 700 and 5 dribbles the ball to 600 multiplied by nine.

6. 600 multiplied by nine passes the ball to 235 times two. 235 times two dribbles the ball to 100 divided into 6300.

7. 100 divided into 6300 passes the ball to 850 divided by two.

8. 850 divided by two passes the ball to 7400 divided by 100.
   7400 divided by 100 dribbles the ball to 320 multiplied by two.

9. 320 multiplied by two dribbles the ball to 60 times eight.
   60 times eight passes the ball to 500 multiplied by eight.

10. 500 multiplied by eight passes the ball to 24 times three.

11. 24 times three passes the ball to 40 lots of seven.
    40 lots of seven dribbles to 80 multiplied by four.

12. 80 multiplied by four passes the ball to double 580.
    Double 580 dribbles the ball to 40 times 800.

13. 40 times 800 passes the ball to one tenth of 1600.

14. One tenth of 1600 passes the ball to 60 multiplied by 300.
    60 multiplied by 300 passes the ball to 400 times nine.

15. 400 times nine dribbles the ball to 70 times three.
    70 times three passes the ball to 18 multiplied by six.

16. The whistle blows. Put each team's score in the boxes at the bottom of the sheet.

17. Write your name under the winning team's score.

Answers

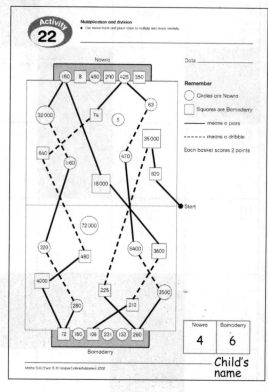

Discussion questions

↓ Who won the game? (Bomaderry)

↓ What is 24 times three and 40 lots of seven? (72/280)

■ Tell me two numbers where the ball was passed/dribbled between the players.

■ Choose a number from the Nowra team and tell me what two numbers multiplied together will give you that number.

↑ Choose a number from the sheet and tell me what number it is a multiple of. How do you know?

↑ Which numbers did not get to handle the ball during the game? (5, 8, 133, 180, 231, 290, 350, 450, 72 000) Choose one of these numbers and put it into a multiplication/division calculation.

Multiplication and division
■ Use known facts and place value to multiply and divide mentally.

Date _____

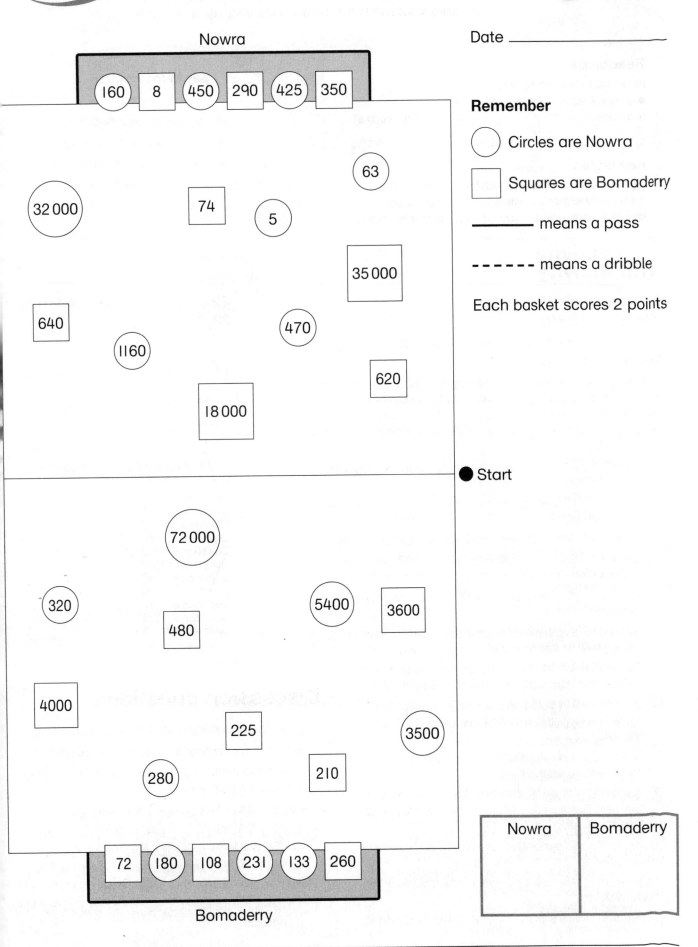

Nowra

160 · 8 · 450 · 290 · 425 · 350

63

32 000 · 74 · 5

35 000

640 · 1160 · 470 · 620

18 000

● Start

72 000

320 · 480 · 5400 · 3600

4000 · 225 · 3500

280 · 210

72 · 180 · 108 · 231 · 133 · 260

Bomaderry

Remember

◯ Circles are Nowra

▢ Squares are Bomaderry

────── means a pass

- - - - - - means a dribble

Each basket scores 2 points

Nowra	Bomaderry

Problems involving 'real life' and measures

■ Use all four operations to solve simple word problems involving numbers and quantities based on 'real life' and measures, using one or more steps.

Resources

Provide each child with the following:

■ a copy of Activity 23 pupil sheet
■ a coloured pencil
■ a pencil
■ a calculator (optional)

Key words

zero, one, two…one thousand   subtract   multiply   divide
quarters   three quarters   one fifth   one eighth   tenths
kilometre   mile   minute   hour   o'clock   quarter to   halfway

Say to the children:

Listen carefully.

I am going to tell you some things to do.

I will say them only once, so listen very carefully.

Do only the things you are told to do and nothing else.

If you make a mistake, cross it out. Do not use an eraser.

There are 12 parts to this activity.

The activity

1. Write your name at the top of the sheet.

This activity is similar to bingo.

2. I want you to colour any five numbers on the sheet.

These are your bingo numbers.

I am going to read out some word problems. You have to work out each answer. If the answer is one of your bingo numbers, you draw a cross through that number. If the answer is not one of your bingo numbers, you have to write the answer on the wastepaper basket. When you have crossed out all five of your numbers call out 'Bingo!'

3. Ready? Question 1 – Glasses come in boxes of six. How many glasses will I get if I buy eight boxes?

4. Question 2 – Michael had 28 children at his party. If 19 were boys, how many were girls?

5. Question 3 – Brian is 44 years old. How old will he be in 35 years?

6. Question 4 – Sarah has travelled 96 miles of a 332 mile journey. How many more miles must she travel to reach halfway?

7. Question 5 – If 17 oranges are cut into quarters, how many pieces will there be?

8. Question 6 – If each song lasts about three minutes, how many songs can you fit on a three-hour tape?

9. Question 7 – A theatre has twelve rows of 20 seats on each of three floors. How many seats are in the theatre?

10. Question 8 – A cyclist has to travel 108 kilometres. If she travels nine kilometres every hour, how many hours will it take her?

11. Question 9 – How many minutes have passed from one o'clock to quarter to three?

12. Question 10 – Of the 60 children in Year 5, three quarters have pets. 26 have a dog. 14 have a cat. How many children have other kinds of pets?

Continue until a child has crossed out all four of their numbers and has called out 'Bingo!'

Check the child's sheet with the answers in the facsimile of the completed sheet.

If time allows continue until you have read out all ten questions.

Answers

Problems involving 'real life' and measures
■ Use all four operations to solve simple word problems involving numbers and quantities based on 'real life' and measures, using one or more steps.

Child's name

Date _____

79	48	12	720	5
68	70	105	9	60

Working out

Children's sheets will vary depending on the numbers coloured.

Answers
Question 1   48
Question 2   9
Question 3   79
Question 4   70
Question 5   68
Question 6   60
Question 7   720
Question 8   12
Question 9   105
Question 10   5

Maths Drill (Year 5) © HarperCollinsPublishers 2003

Discussion questions

↓ How many of your bingo numbers did you cross out?

↓ Tell me one of the bingo numbers you crossed out.

■ Look at your working out. Choose a calculation you worked out and explain to us what you did.

■ Which numbers did you write on the wastepaper basket?

↑ Question 4 was: Sarah has travelled 96 miles of a 332 mile journey. How many more miles must she travel to reach halfway? What was the answer? (70) How did you work it out? Did anyone work it out a different way?

↑ Choose one of the numbers you did not colour and put it into a word problem.

Problems involving 'real life' and measures

■ Use all four operations to solve simple word problems involving numbers and quantities based on 'real life' and measures, using one or more steps.

Date _____

79	48	12	720	5
68	70	105	9	60

Working out

Problems involving money

- Use all four operations to solve simple word problems involving numbers and quantities based on money, using one or more steps, including making simple conversions of pounds to foreign currency and finding simple percentages.

Resources

Provide each child with the following:

- a copy of Activity 24 pupil sheet
- a pencil
- working out paper (optional)
- a calculator (optional)

Key words

zero, one, two…one thousand   pence   pounds   coins   total cost   costs   save   change   half-price   spend   spent share   per cent

Say to the children:

Listen carefully.

I am going to tell you some things to do.

I will say them only once, so listen very carefully.

Do only the things you are told to do and nothing else.

If you make a mistake, cross it out. Do not use an eraser.

There are 13 parts to this activity.

The activity

1. Look at question one. Work out the answer and write it on coin number one.

2. Look at question two. Work out the answer and write it on coin number two.

3. Look at question four. Work out the answer and write it on coin number five.

4. Look at question eight. Work out the answer and write it on coin number nine.

5. Look at question eleven. Work out the answer and write it on coin number twelve.

6. Look at question fourteen. Work out the answer and write it on coin number six.

7. Look at question twelve. Work out the answer and write it on coin number ten.

8. Look at question three. Work out the answer and write it on coin number fourteen.

9. Look at question seven. Work out the answer and write it on coin number three.

10. Look at question ten. Work out the answer and write it in coin number fifteen.

11. Look at question fifteen. Work out the answer and write it on coin number eight.

12. Look at question five. Work out the answer and write it on coin number eleven.

13. Write your name on coin number sixteen.

Answers

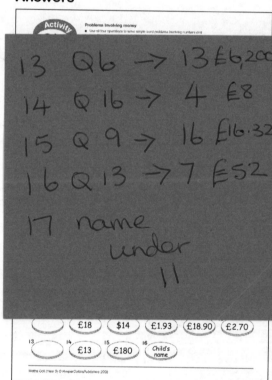

Discussion questions

↓ What did you write on coin number nine? ($14)

↓ Where did you write ninety-nine pence? (coin 6)

■ Choose one of the word problems you solved. What is the answer? How did you work it out? Did anyone work it out a different way?

■ What is the answer to question ten? (£180) How did you work it out? Did anyone work it out a different way?

↑ Look at one of the word problems you did not answer. What is the answer?

↑ Look at the coins. What is the total of coins one, two and six? (£33.13)

Activity 24

Problems involving money

■ Use all four operations to solve simple word problems involving numbers and quantities based on money, using one or more steps, including making simple conversions of pounds to foreign currency and finding simple percentages.

Date _____

1 What is the total of £10.06, £18.37 and £3.13?

2
10 for £5.80

How much does one cost?

3 Brooke saved 25p a week for one year. How many pounds did she save?

4 A video costs £32.60. What change do I get from £50?

5 A CD at half price now costs £9.45. What was the original price?

6 Four people share a lottery win of £24 800. How much does each person get?

7
Sandwich	£2.37
Drink	£1.40
Fruit	80p
Crisps	65p
Chocolate	95p

Troy spent £4.42. What did he buy?

8
Travel to Australia
Exchange Rate £1 = $2.80

How many Australian dollars do I get for £5?

9 What is the cost of 136 pencils at 12p each?

10 The deposit on a £360 bed is 50%. How much is the deposit?

11 In his piggy bank Jamie has twelve 5p coins, six 10p coins and three 50p coins. How much money does he have altogether?

12 A bottle of lemonade costs £1.48 and a large bag of crisps costs £1.59. What change do I get from £5?

13 Find the total of 69p, 38p, 87p and £3.26.

14 What is my change from £5 if I spent £2.50 and £1.51?

15 Three people paid £54 for a harbour cruise. What was the cost of each ticket?

16 There is 25% off prices in a sale. How much do you get off £32?

SALE! 25% off everything!

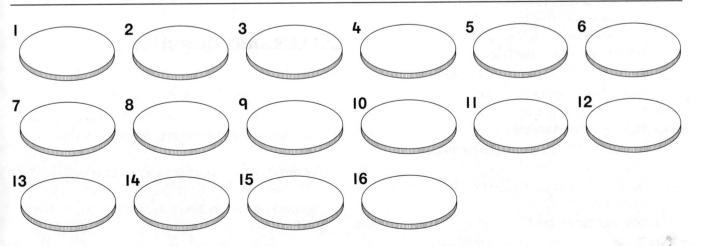

Year 5 Measures

Length, mass and capacity

- Use, read and write standard metric units (km, m, cm, mm, kg, g, l, ml), including their abbreviations, and relationships between them.
- Convert larger to smaller units (e.g. km to m, m to cm or mm, kg to g, l to ml).
- Know imperial units (mile, pint, gallon).

Resources

Provide each child with the following:
- a copy of Activity 25 pupil sheet
- a pencil

Key words

zero, one, two...ten thousand   decimal   point   kilometre
metre   centimetre   millimetre   kilogram   gram   litre   millilitre
mile   pint   gallon   approximately   half   one quarter
three quarters   one tenth   one hundredth

Say to the children:

Listen carefully.

I am going to tell you some things to do.

I will say them only once, so listen very carefully.

Do only the things you are told to do and nothing else.

If you make a mistake, cross it out. Do not use an eraser.

There are 19 parts to this activity.

The activity

1. How many metres are there in one kilometre? Write the answer in box one.
2. How many centimetres are there in one metre? Write the answer in box two.
3. How many millimetres are there in one metre? Write the answer in box four.
4. How many millimetres are there in one centimetre? Write the answer in box six.
5. How many grams are there in one kilogram? Write the answer in box nine.
6. How many millilitres are there in one litre? Write the answer in box 13.
7. Approximately how many metres are there in ¼ km? Write the answer in box 20.
8. Approximately how many millilitres are there in ½ litre? Write the answer in box five.
9. Approximately how many ml are there in 3½ L? Write the answer in box 14.
10. How many centimetres are there in half a metre? Write the answer in box seven.
11. How many grams are there in one quarter of a kilogram? Write the answer in box 18.
12. How many millilitres are there in three quarters of a litre? Write the answer in box three.
13. How many centimetres are there in one tenth of a metre? Write the answer in box 16.
14. How many grams are there in one hundredth of a kilogram? Write the answer in box 10.
15. How many centimetres are there in 1.8 metres? Write the answer in box 12.
16. How many grams are there in 4.6 kilograms? Write the answer in box eight.
17. How many metres are there in 385 centimetres? Write the answer in box 15.
18. How many litres are there in 2500 millilitres? Write the answer in box 11.
19. Write your name in box 17.

Answers

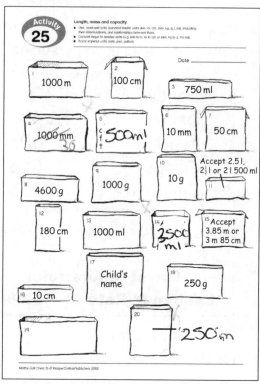

Discussion questions

↓ What did you write in box one? (1000 m)

↓ Where did you write 1000 millilitres? (box 13)

■ How many grams are there in one quarter of a kilogram? (250 g)

■ How many millilitres are there in three quarters of a litre? (750 ml)

↑ Approximately how many metres are there in a mile? (from 1500 m to 1600 m)

↑ How many millilitres are there in four and three quarter litres? (4750 ml)

Length, mass and capacity

- Use, read and write standard metric units (km, m, cm, mm, kg, g, l, ml), including their abbreviations, and relationships between them.
- Convert larger to smaller units (e.g. km to m, m to cm or mm, kg to g, l to ml).
- Know imperial units (mile, pint, gallon).

Date _____

Area and perimeter

- Understand area measured in square centimetres (cm²).
- Understand and use the formula in words 'length × breadth' for the area of a rectangle.
- Understand, measure and calculate perimeters of rectangles and regular polygons.

Resources

Provide each child with the following:
- a copy of Activity 26 pupil sheet
- a red, blue, green and yellow coloured pencil
- a pencil
- a calculator (optional)

Key words

zero, one, two…one hundred   area   perimeter   centimetre
square centimetre (cm²)   point

Say to the children:

Listen carefully.

I am going to tell you some things to do.

I will say them only once, so listen very carefully.

Do only the things you are told to do and nothing else.

If you make a mistake, cross it out. Do not use an eraser.

There are 12 parts to this activity.

The activity

1. Look at shape A. What is the area of shape A? Write the answer inside the shape.

2. Look at shape B. What is the perimeter of shape B? Write the answer inside the shape.

3. Which shape has an area of 17.1 square centimetres? Colour that shape blue.

4. Which shape has a perimeter of 28.4 centimetres? Colour that shape yellow.

5. Look at shape C. What is the area of shape C? Write the answer inside the shape.

6. Look at shape F. What is the perimeter of shape F? Write the answer inside the shape.

7. Which shape has an area of 25.92 square centimetres? Colour that shape red.

8. Which shape has a perimeter of 19.8 centimetres? Colour that shape green.

9. Look at shape D. What is the area of shape D? Write the answer inside the shape.

10. Look at shape E. What is the perimeter of shape E? Write the answer inside the shape.

11. Which shape has an area of 76.26 square centimetres? Write your name inside that shape.

12. Which shape has a perimeter of 21 centimetres? Write the answer inside that shape.

Answers

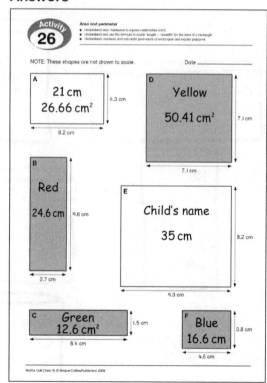

Discussion questions

↓ Which shape did you colour green? (C)

↓ Choose any shape and tell me the area/perimeter of that shape.

■ What is the perimeter of shape B? (24.6 cm) What is the area of shape B? (25.92 square centimetres)

■ Which shapes have a perimeter less than 25 centimetres? (A, B, C, F)

↑ Which shape has the largest/smallest area? (E/C) Which shape has the largest/smallest perimeter? (E/F)

↑ Look at the area of each shape. Tell me the shapes in order of size largest to smallest. (E, D, A, B, F, C)

Area and perimeter

- Understand area measured in square centimetres (cm²).
- Understand and use the formula in words 'length × breadth' for the area of a rectangle.
- Understand, measure and calculate perimeters of rectangles and regular polygons.

NOTE: These shapes are not drawn to scale.

Date _____

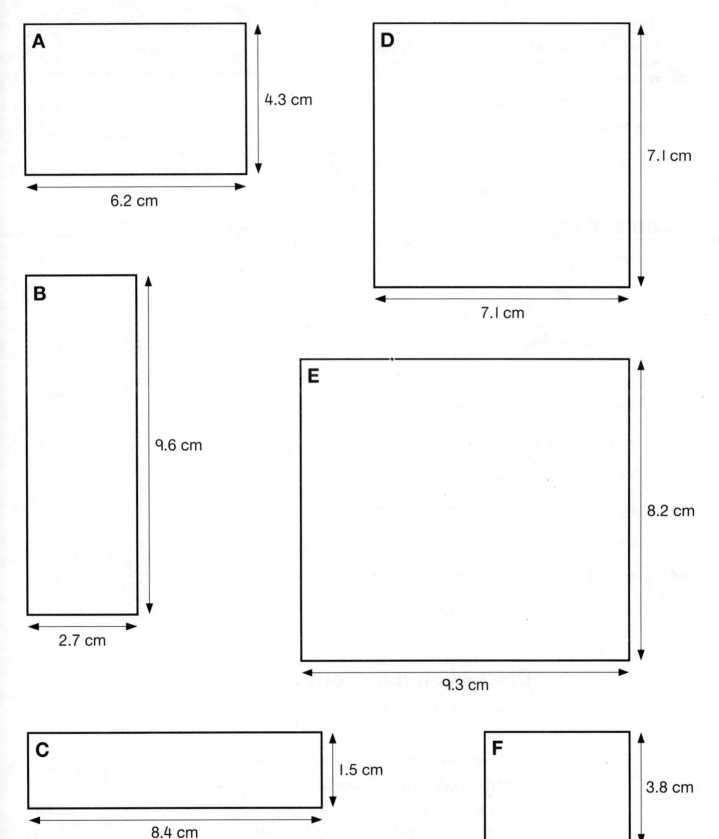

A 4.3 cm — 6.2 cm

B 9.6 cm — 2.7 cm

C 1.5 cm — 8.4 cm

D 7.1 cm — 7.1 cm

E 8.2 cm — 9.3 cm

F 3.8 cm — 4.5 cm

Year 5 Measures

Time

■ Read the time on a 24-hour digital clock and use 24-hour clock notation, such as 19:53.

Resources

Provide each child with the following:
■ a copy of Activity 27 pupil sheet
■ a pencil

Key words

clock analogue digital time minutes hour o'clock past to morning afternoon night

Say to the children:

Listen carefully.

I am going to tell you some things to do.

I will say them only once, so listen very carefully.

Do only the things you are told to do and nothing else.

If you make a mistake, cross it out. Do not use an eraser.

There are 11 parts to this activity.

The activity

1. Look at the time on Clock A. Show that time on Clock E.

2. Look at Clock C. Show the time of twelve minutes past seven in the morning.

3. Look at the time on Clock J. Show that time on Clock I.

4. Look at Clock H. Show the time of twenty-four minutes past ten at night.

5. Look at the time on Clock N. Show that time on Clock D.

6. Look at Clock G. Show the time of twenty minutes to four in the afternoon.

7. Look at the time on Clock L. Show that time on Clock F.

8. Look at Clock O. Show the time of ten minutes to two in the morning.

9. Look at the time on Clock B. Show that time on Clock K.

10. Look at Clock M. Show the time of quarter to five in the afternoon.

11. Write your name under the clock that reads twenty minutes to four.

Answers

Discussion questions

↓ What does the time on Clock F read? (9 minutes past 1)

↓ Choose a clock and tell me the time.

■ Look at clock D. What time does it show? (14 minutes to 4)

■ Which clock shows the time of ten minutes to two? (Clock O)

↑ Look at Clock J. How many hours and minutes will pass before it shows the time on Clock N? (4 hours and 41 minutes)

↑ Look at Clock I. What time will it read in 10/20/30/45 minutes time? (11:15/11:25/11:35/11:50)

Time

■ Read the time on a 24-hour digital clock and use 24-hour clock notation, such as 19:53.

Date _____

Time
■ Use timetables.

Resources

Provide each child with the following:
■ a copy of Activity 28 pupil sheet
■ a pencil

Key words

time   minutes   o'clock   past   to   arrive   leave

Say to the children:

Listen carefully.

I am going to tell you some things to do.

I will say them only once, so listen very carefully.

Do only the things you are told to do and nothing else.

If you make a mistake, cross it out. Do not use an eraser.

There are 15 parts to this activity.

The activity

1. What time does the last train leave Central? Write the answer on ticket number one.

2. How long does it take the one minute past seven train from Central to reach Sutherland? Write the answer on ticket number two.

3. Which train would you need to catch from Central to arrive at Helensburgh by ten o'clock? Write the answer on ticket number three.

4. How long does it take the five fifty-five train from Central to travel from Hurstville to Stanwell Park? Write the answer on ticket number four.

5. How many stops does the six twenty-four train from Central make? Write the answer on ticket number five.

6. If I get on the train at seven minutes past eight at Sutherland, where would I arrive at eight forty-three? Write the answer on ticket number six.

7. How many trains stop at Waterfall? Write the answer on ticket number seven.

8. How long does it take the eight minutes past nine train to travel from Central to Scarborough? Write the answer on ticket number eight.

9. How many trains go through from Central to Scarborough? Write the answer on ticket number nine.

10. Which trains go from Central to Redfern? Write the answer on ticket number ten.

11. If I get on the train at seven minutes past eight at Sutherland, what time will I arrive at Scarborough? Write the answer on ticket number eleven.

12. If I live in Hurstville and have to be in Stanwell Park by quarter past ten, which train should I take? Write the answer on ticket number twelve.

13. Write your name on ticket number thirteen.

14. How long does it take the seven fifty-eight train from Central to travel from Hurstville to Helensburgh? Write the answer on ticket number fourteen.

15. At which station does the train stop at ten to seven? Write the answer on ticket number fifteen.

Answers

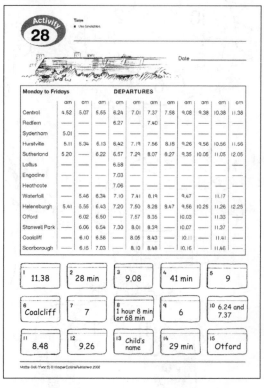

Discussion questions

↓ What did you write on ticket number seven? (7)

↓ How many trains go from Central to Scarborough? (6)

■ Which trains go from Central to Redfern? (6:24 and 7:37)

■ At which station does the train stop at ten to seven? (Otford)

↑ How long does it take the seven fifty-eight train to travel from Hurstville to Helensburgh? (29 min)

↑ Tell me something about the timetable.

Date _____

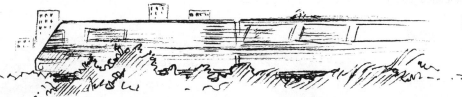

Monday to Fridays	DEPARTURES										
	am	am	am	am	am	am	am	am	am	am	am
Central	4.52	5.07	5.55	6.24	7.01	7.37	7.58	9.08	9.38	10.38	11.38
Redfern	—	—	—	6.27	—	7.40	—	—	—	—	—
Sydenham	5.01	—	—	—	—	—	—	—	—	—	—
Hurstville	5.11	5.34	6.13	6.42	7.19	7.56	8.18	9.26	9.56	10.56	11.56
Sutherland	5.20	—	6.22	6.57	7.29	8.07	8.27	9.35	10.05	11.05	12.05
Loftus	—	—	—	6.58	—	—	—	—	—	—	—
Engadine	—	—	—	7.03	—	—	—	—	—	—	—
Heathcote	—	—	—	7.06	—	—	—	—	—	—	—
Waterfall	—	5.46	6.34	7.10	7.41	8.19	—	9.47	—	11.17	—
Helensburgh	5.41	5.55	6.43	7.20	7.50	8.28	8.47	9.56	10.25	11.26	12.25
Otford	—	6.02	6.50	—	7.57	8.35	—	10.03	—	11.33	—
Stanwell Park	—	6.06	6.54	7.30	8.01	8.39	—	10.07	—	11.37	—
Coalcliff	—	6.10	6.58	—	8.05	8.43	—	10.11	—	11.41	—
Scarborough	—	6.15	7.03	—	8.10	8.48	—	10.16	—	11.46	—

1

2

3

4

5

6

7

8

9

10

11

12

13

14

15

Reflective symmetry

■ Complete symmetrical patterns with two lines of symmetry at right angles (using squared paper or pegboard).

Resources

Provide each child with the following:
■ a copy of Activity 29 pupil sheet
■ a red, blue, green and yellow coloured pencil

Key words

zero, one, two…one hundred   symmetry   line of symmetry
right angle   pattern

Say to the children:

Listen carefully.

I am going to tell you some things to do.

I will say them only once, so listen very carefully.

Do only the things you are told to do and nothing else.

If you make a mistake, cross it out. Do not use an eraser.

There are 15 parts to this activity.

The activity

1. Find the number three. Colour the square green.

2. Find the number 11. Colour the square green.

3. Find the number 27. Colour the square yellow.

4. Find the number 28. Colour the square blue.

5. Find the number 31. Colour the square red.

6. Find the number 33. Colour the square blue.

7. Find the number 37. Colour the square green.

8. Write your name under the line near the word Name.

9. Find the number 53. Colour the square yellow.

10. Find the number 65. Colour the square red.

11. Find the number 69. Colour the square green.

12. Find the number 79. Colour the square yellow.

13. Find the number 85. Colour the square green.

14. Find the number 88. Colour the square red.

15. Look at the two lines of symmetry. Using your coloured pencils complete the symmetrical pattern.

Answers

1	2	G3	4	5	6	7	G8	9	10	
G11	12	R13	14	G15	G16	17	R18	19	G20	
21	Y22	B23	Y24	25	26	Y27	B28	Y29	30	
R31	G32	B33	G34	R35	R36	G37	B38	G39	R40	
41	42	Y43	44	45	46	47	Y48	49	50	
51	52	Y53	54	55	56	57	Y58	59	60	
R61	G62	B63	G64	R65	R66	G67	B68	G69	R70	
71	Y72	B73	Y74	75	76	Y77	B78	Y79	80	
G81	82	R83	84	G85	G86	87	R88	89	G90	
91	92	G93	94	95	96	97	G98	99	100	

B Blue
G Green
R Red
Y Yellow

Activity 29 — Reflective symmetry

Name _____   Date _____

Maths Call (Year 5) © HarperCollinsPublishers 2002

Discussion questions

↓ What colour is number 39? (green)

↓ Tell me a number you did not colour.

■ Which numbers did you colour red?
(13, 18, 31, 35, 36, 40, 61, 65, 66, 70, 83, 88)

■ Does your pattern look symmetrical? Why? Why not?

↑ If you were to colour the number 46 orange, what other numbers would you need to colour orange? (45, 55, 56)

↑ Choose a number that you have coloured. What other three numbers are symmetrical to that number?

Reflective symmetry

■ Complete symmetrical patterns with two lines of symmetry
   at right angles (using squared paper or pegboard).

Name _____   Date _____

1	2	3	4	5	6	7	8	9	10
11	12	13	14	15	16	17	18	19	20
21	22	23	24	25	26	27	28	29	30
31	32	33	34	35	36	37	38	39	40
41	42	43	44	45	46	47	48	49	50
51	52	53	54	55	56	57	58	59	60
61	62	63	64	65	66	67	68	69	70
71	72	73	74	75	76	77	78	79	80
81	82	83	84	85	86	87	88	89	90
91	92	93	94	95	96	97	98	99	100

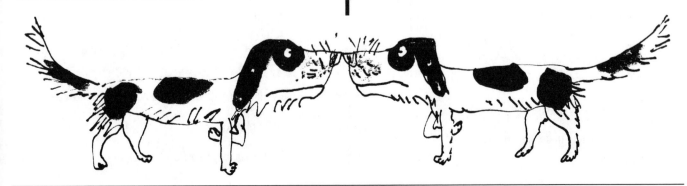

Maths Call (Year 5) © HarperCollins*Publishers* 2002

Position and direction

■ Read and plot co-ordinates in the first quadrant.

Resources

Provide each child with the following:
■ a copy of Activity 30 pupil sheet
■ a pencil

Key words

zero, one, two...eight   co-ordinates   *x*-axis   *y*-axis

Say to the children:

Listen carefully.

I am going to tell you some things to do.

I will say them only once, so listen very carefully.

Do only the things you are told to do and nothing else.

If you make a mistake, cross it out. Do not use an eraser.

There are 21 parts to this activity.

The activity

1. Draw a cross at the co-ordinate (1, 6).

2. Draw a cross at the co-ordinate (3, 5).

3. Draw a ring around the co-ordinate (4, 3).

4. Draw a ring around the co-ordinate (8, 4).

5. Draw a cross at the co-ordinate (6, 1).

6. Draw ring around the co-ordinate (5, 3).

7. Draw a ring around the co-ordinate (6, 5).

8. Draw a cross at the co-ordinate (4, 2).

9. Draw a cross at the co-ordinate (2, 1).

10. Draw a ring around the co-ordinate (7, 7).

11. Draw a cross at the co-ordinate (5, 5).

12. Draw a ring around the co-ordinate (4, 7).

13. Draw a ring around the co-ordinate (8, 1).

14. Draw a cross at the co-ordinate (6, 8).

15. Draw a cross at the co-ordinate (1, 2).

16. Draw a ring around the co-ordinate (1, 4).

17. Draw a cross at the co-ordinate (7, 0).

18. Draw a ring around the co-ordinate (4, 5).

19. Draw a ring around the co-ordinate (3, 8).

20. Draw a cross at the co-ordinate (8, 6).

21. Write your name under the number five on the *x*-axis.

Answers

Discussion questions

↓ Tell me a co-ordinate where you have marked an *x*.

↓ Tell me a co-ordinate you drew a ring around.

■ Look at the number six on the *y*-axis. What points did you mark on this line? (1, 6) and (8, 6)

■ Where did you write your name? (Under the number five on the *x*-axis.)

↑ What point did you mark at zero? (7, 0)

↑ Which is the *x*-axis? Which is the *y*-axis?

Position and direction

■ Read and plot co-ordinates in the first quadrant.

Date _____

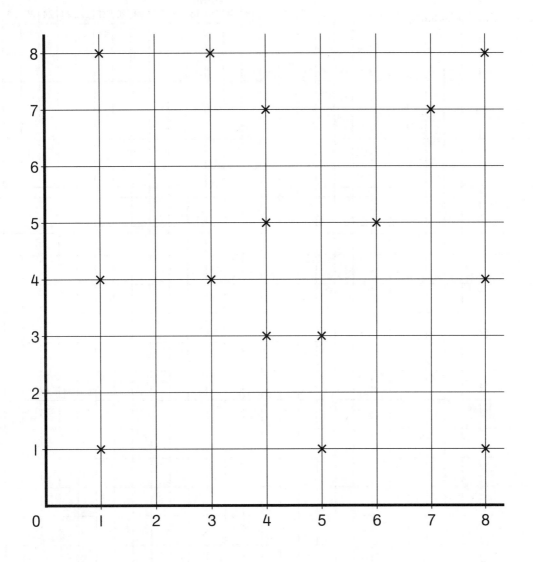

Maths Call assessment sheet

YEAR
CLASS
TEACHER

/ Not understood   ∠ Developing an understanding   △ Completely understood

NAME	ACTIVITY																													
	1	2	3	4	5	6	7	8	9	10	11	12	13	14	15	16	17	18	19	20	21	22	23	24	25	26	27	28	29	30